# THE NATURE
# OF PHYSICAL THEORY

BY

## P. W. BRIDGMAN

*Hollis Professor of Mathematics and Natural Philosophy*
*Harvard University*

PUBLISHED ON
THE LOUIS CLARK VANUXEM FOUNDATION

DOVER PUBLICATIONS

NEW YORK

# PREFACE

*THE following pages contain in expanded form the substance of three Vanuxem lectures given at Princeton University in December 1935. They must be taken quite literally at their face value as representing the present stage of my own personal attempt as an experimental physicist to appreciate more clearly what are the possibilities open to us in our endeavor to reduce the material of experimental physics to order and understandability. The attempt has been forced by recent developments—the failures of earlier ideals and theories and the very obviously divergent aims and ideals and practices of many of those contemporary physicists whose speculations are influential. No pretension at all is made to scholarly competence or to a systematic examination and critique of the speculations of others in this field; no doubt points of view will be found elaborated in perhaps unnecessary detail which have been familiar for some time to technical logicians, mathematicians, and philosophers. However, the mere fact that there is such a divergence of belief and practice in the great body of physicists engaged on theoretical matters, and even among the practical mathematicians, is itself evidence that clear thinking on many fundamental matters has not diffused very far. This, and the conviction that many of the fundamental ideas, as far as they are of interest to the physicist or other experimentalist, can be stated in simple language, without the formidable apparatus of the technical logician, must be the excuse for the following naïve pages.*

P. W. Bridgman

# CONTENTS

# I. INTRODUCTORY

IN THIS volume we shall be primarily concerned with a critical analysis of the points of view and the methods which we adopt in trying to understand the simpler aspects of the ever-changing spectacle about us. We shall perhaps arbitrarily restrict ourselves to those aspects which are ordinarily understood to be within the domain of physics. It is a commonplace that at least a moderate amount of analysis and criticism of our fundamental methods is becoming more and more indispensable if we are to achieve even the most modest success in dealing with the increasing complexity of our physical surroundings.

This increasing complexity has a twofold aspect. In the first place there is the tremendously increased complexity of purely factual knowledge, as we probe further and further with our physical measurements. X-rays, electrons, radioactivity, relativity, crystal structure, cosmic rays, wave mechanics, low temperatures, positive electrons, isotopes, neutrons, atomic synthesis, induced radioactivity, suggest revolutionary additions to factual knowledge that have occurred within the memory of perhaps most of us. Each addition to factual knowledge demands that we try to fit it into our scheme of things, and that we construct some sort of theory of the new phenomenon. It is only too well known to us that we have found that many of the new phenomena could not be fitted in without fundamental revision of theories previously thought adequate. A great number of theories have thus sprung up, many of them almost complete failures and only a few even partially successful. This increasing body of theory, successful and unsuccessful, constitutes the second aspect of the increasing complexity that confronts us. This aspect of physics is just as important for the physicist as the purely factual aspect in so far as we recognize that the ultimate task of the physicist is to understand.

The attempt to understand why it is that certain types of theory work and others do not is the concern of the physicist as critic, as contrasted with the physicist as theorist. The material for the physicist as critic is the body of physical theory, just as the material of the physicist as theorist is the body of experimental knowledge. We shall be almost entirely concerned here with the critical activities of the physicist. It seems to me that there is a fundamental difference in kind between his critical and theoretical activities. It is the task of theoretical physics to compress all experimental knowledge into an understandable point of view; the theorist can never foresee what the experimenter will find when his range is extended to include fields at present inaccessible, so that he must always regard his last and most successful theory as a structure of limited validity, always subject to the necessity for radical alteration when extended to include such new experimental facts as may be later discovered. Furthermore, increasing complexity of experimental knowledge imposes a more and more formidable task on the theorist, so that we may expect his progress to become increasingly difficult.

The task of the critic on the other hand is essentially limited in character, for his task may be broadly defined to be to map out the possibilities and the limitations of the human mind in dealing with the problems presented to it. In so far as we may assume that the human mind has approximately fixed and definite properties and is not in such a rapid state of evolution that it runs away from us during the discussion, we are not here confronted with unlimited possibilities of complexity, but the field is an essentially closed one. Thus it seems to me entirely conceivable that after a certain amount of reflection on the material in hand, we may be able to arrive at a notion of our limitations and possibilities sufficiently good for our immediate purpose, and that having acquired this amount of understanding, we may then pass on, leaving criticism behind us as a well rounded and more or less definitive discipline. Of course, it is absurd to maintain that even in criticism one can hope to arrive at a structure perfect in all respects and not capable of constant improvement or elaboration; neither can one maintain that the subject has not an intrinsic interest which would justify the philosopher in elevating it into a self-contained and independent activity. But for me as a physicist, criticism is an enterprise entered into solely for practical reasons, because I find myself forced into it by the failures of my preconceptions in many practical situations. As a matter of observation I can already discern the operation of the law of diminishing returns here, and it is my hope that I can eventually have done with criticism and pass on to something else. In this effort it seems to me that our chances of success are greatly increased by the increase of observational material offered to our hands by the increase in the body of physical theory of recent years; here increasing complexity of material certainly increases our chance of success instead of continually pushing away from us the final goal, as does increasing complexity of experimental knowledge.

Not only is it possible that the individual physicist will be able to learn his criticism, and having learned it, think of it no more, but it is even conceivable that as a self-conscious enterprise it may vanish from the education of physicists after a few generations. For a large part of our education consists in unconsciously acquiring the ability to imitate the methods which our companions have found to be successful, and if all the theories which are presented to our future physicist for observation are constructed on a basis of sound criticism, he will acquire instinctively and without conscious effort the art of properly constructing his theories. In fact, the younger generation of physicists, born since the special theory of relativity was formulated, do seem to have to a large degree just this instinctive ability to proceed safely, and no doubt to them many of our considerations in the following will appear trite and uninteresting. But it seems to me that our present theories, even the successful ones, are not yet constructed so completely in accord with sound principles but that in this day and generation criticism is a most necessary and useful enterprise for the physicist. One could document this contention, if necessary, by a chamber of horrors taken from the work of living physicists.

The physicist cannot lay claim to any essentially new discoveries in his awakening critical self-consciousness, and we cannot pretend that most of what we are discovering to be important has not already been clearly apprehended by some of the great speculative minds among the technical logicians and mathematicians or even the physicists themselves. But certainly any such apprehension has not been very widely disseminated, and has hitherto percolated only to a very small extent in the direction of the ordinary physicist, overwhelmed with all the new factual things crowding about him. In these pages I explicitly disclaim having anything to say to the technical logician; I can speak only from the point of view of the awakening awareness coming to the physicist. I do think, however, that this awakening awareness contains the possibilities of very important reactions on the conduct of our daily lives in domains remote from that of physics, so that perhaps this volume may help in popularizing the ability to handle actual situations, although it may offer no new technical contribution. It may, however, well require generations of intensive education before the rational principles of thought which are necessary for dealing with the simple situations of physics are intuitively grasped and instinctively applied to the complex situations of social life.

# II. OPERATIONS

THE incentive to our present burst of critical activity doubtless had its origin in the disconcerting discovery, made in analyzing the reasons for the success of the restricted principle of relativity, that some of our fundamental concepts and modes of thought were incapable of dealing with the enlarged physical situations that were developing. Out of this has come one of the principal demands that the critic must set himself, namely to get his physical thinking on such a secure basis that this sort of thing may not happen again, and to make his methods elastic enough to deal with any sort of factual situation that may present itself. Our analysis of one of the fundamental reasons for the success of the restricted theory of relativity has disclosed a method of meeting this demand which must, I think, remain at the foundation of all our efforts at criticism. This method was suggested by the clear recognition that the ultimately important thing about any theory is what it actually does, not what it says it does or what its author thinks it does, for these are often very different things indeed. The most important technique of criticism is the technique of clearly apprehending and reporting just what one actually does, or what is actually happening in any situation, and this is a technique which is not easy to acquire and in which one becomes more expert only by continual practice. One reason why criticism is now in such a more advantageous position than it was thirty years ago is that it has now so much more material, in the accumulating bulk of physical theories, for the practice of this technique.

A clear-eyed recognition of what actually happens is hindered by most of the mental habits drilled into us by education. For I think it must be conceded that the major part of education at present consists in acquiring the *intuitive* ability to handle the conceptual instruments which the human race has evolved to meet the situations with which it is confronted, such, for example, as the all embracing instrument of language, whereas it is just these conceptual instruments that enlarged experience is proving are faulty. It is often very difficult indeed to get away from unconscious verbal implications that we have accepted without analysis all our lives, particularly when, as in many cases, our success as social beings depends on the completeness with which these implications are ingrained into our conduct. Not only do verbal implications hinder us in giving an accurate account of situations, but it is often difficult to get rid of the inferences with which we unconsciously dress our direct observation, as an analysis of the circumstantial evidence of many court proceedings would bring out.

Not only is it difficult to strip away the implications and give perfectly straight statements of what happens, but having done this the results are often so distressingly obvious that it is difficult to believe that we have uncovered anything of significance. But the most simple and apparently innocent statements often do contain a wealth of significance that may have bearing on everything that we do. It requires practice, imagination, and insight to perceive that the most obvious observations, such for example, as "thinking is an activity of the human nervous system" may contain revolutionary implications.

Most difficult of all—more difficult than the analysis or the intellectual recognition of significance—is the emotional acceptance of what we have discovered as really making a difference, and altering in accord with such acceptance our inmost convictions and mode of conduct. Probably every one of us has experienced the extreme slowness with which preconceptions which were acquired unconsciously in childhood wear away, even under the most determined and well considered attack by intelligence. Yet it is not until the convictions that we acquire become living convictions or, in everyday language, not until they "get under our skins," do they really matter; not until then can we hope to make real progress with the results of our analysis. In this respect the younger generation is enviably better off than those of us who have had to acquire these things by conscious effort— the younger generation is born with some of these things already under its skin.

There is one phase of the technique by which analysis makes itself conscious of what it actually does in any situation, and which is an outgrowth of relativity theory, which seems to me to be especially important. This technique I have called "operational" and I have discussed certain aspects of it at some length in my book, *The Logic of Modern Physics*, and have elaborated other aspects in other places.[1] This point of view will be implicit in much of what follows, so that it will pay to pause for a brief elaboration of the idea.

The best way to make it apprehensible, perhaps, is to give a paraphrase of what actually happened when Einstein formulated the special theory of relativity. In seeking to set up a theory of certain effects in moving bodies, Einstein found it desirable, as we practically always do in constructing a quantitative theory, to start with mathematical equations. The important step that Einstein made was that in analyzing the connection of the equations with the theory he was led to examine the details of what we do in applying the equations in any specific case. In particular, one of the variables in the equations was the time—what do we do in obtaining the number which replaces the general symbol for time when we apply the equation to a concrete case? As physicists

[1] "A Physicist's Second Reaction to Mengenlehre," *Scripta Mathematica*, Vol. II, 1934.

we know that this number is obtained by reading a clock of some sort, that is, it is a number given by a prescribed physical operation. Or the equations may involve the times of two different events in two different places, and to understand completely what is now involved we must analyze what we do in determining the time of two such events. Analysis shows that we read two clocks, one at each place. A new element now enters, because a complete description of all the manipulations involved demands that we set up some method by which we compare the two clocks with which we measure the two events. Out of the examination of what we do in comparing the clocks we all know came Einstein's revolutionary recognition that the property of two events which hitherto had been unthinkingly called simultaneity involves in the doing a complicated sequence of physical operations which cannot be uniquely specified unless we specify who it is that is reading the clocks. We know that a consequence of this is that different observers do not always get the same result, so that simultaneity is not an absolute property of two events, but is relative to the observing system, that is, the system that does the things that constitute the measurement. What Einstein was in effect doing in this instance was to inquire into the meaning of simultaneity, and he was finding the meaning by analyzing the physical operations employed in applying the concept in any concrete instance. It cannot be claimed, I suppose, that Einstein was the first consciously to use this technique; it is simply that the use of it by him occurred under conditions which dramatically focused attention on its importance, so that physicists are now apparently permanently "reconditioned" in this respect.

Two aspects of the question of "meaning" are involved here. There is in the first place a general aspect; with regard to this it seems to me that as a matter of self-analysis I am never sure of a meaning until I have analyzed what I do, so that for me meaning is to be found in a recognition of the activities involved. These activities may be diffused and nebulous and on the purely emotional level, as when I recognize that what I mean when I say that I dislike something is that I confront myself with the thing in actuality or in imagination and observe whether the emotion that it arouses is one with which I associate the name "dislike." The emotion awakened which I call "dislike" permits of no further analysis from this point of view, but has to be accepted as an ultimate. Because the unanalyzable "dislike" involves so much, and because the operation of observing whether the emotion is awakened is so simple, the operational aspect of meaning is not very important in cases like this.

The more particular and important aspect of the operational significance of meaning is suggested by the fact that Einstein recognized that in dealing with physical situations the operations which give meaning to our physical concepts should properly be physical operations, actually carried out. For in so restricting the permissible operations, our theories reduce in the last analysis to descriptions of operations actually carried out in actual situations, and so cannot involve us in inconsistency or contradiction, since these do not occur in actual physical situations. Thus is solved at one stroke the problem of so constructing our fundamental physical concepts that we shall never have to revise them in the light of new experience. New experience can demand only an extension of previously held concepts, not a fundamental revision, because at any moment our concepts are coextensive with the system of existing knowledge. The procedure of Einstein was in sharp contrast with the former method of defining concepts, as for example, the celebrated definition of Newton of absolute time as that which flows uniformly, independent of material happenings. In the first place this definition was in terms of properties, instead of operations, and in the second place the properties themselves had no operational definition in terms of actual physical operations, but were defined in terms of metaphysical and idealized operations, which could therefore contain no assurance that they correspond to what will be found in experience. As a matter of fact they were found not to have such correspondence to a sufficient degree.

In the actual working out of the special theory of relativity much more had to be added than this revised conception of meaning, but the superstructure would not have been possible without the fundamental revision.

It must not be understood that we are maintaining that as a necessity of thought we must always demand that physical concepts be defined in terms of physical operations; we are merely stating that if by convention we agree to use only those concepts in describing physical situations to which we can give a meaning in terms of physical operations, then we are sure that we shall not have to retract. Other sorts of concept may be applicable, but such always require justification, and we cannot be sure that the justification will be forthcoming until we have made the experiment. The convention that physical concepts be defined in terms of physical operations is such an obviously useful one that it is coming to be accepted by physicists and demanded tacitly.

The significance of Einstein's observation about simultaneity and of a similar observation about the measurement of length is often sought in the generalized statement that all measurement is relative, and the implication is that this recognition of the relativity of measurement (which in special relativity means relative to the system of measurement) is intuitively to be accepted. I think there is nothing intuitive or general here, but a detailed and specific examination of what we do in measuring a time or a distance has to be made. The only generalization is that the measurements are relative to the fundamental operations; this is merely a truism and yields nothing.

We have seen that if we restrict the operations we use in describing physical situations to physical operations actually performed, we shall be certain not to land in contradiction. We have also suggested that we may, if we like, give up the certainty of never making mistakes, and construct our concepts in other ways, defining them perhaps in terms of properties, as is so often done in mathematics, and then experiment with the structures we may erect in terms of such concepts to see whether the concepts are useful. We still have operational meaning for our concepts, but the operations are mental operations, and have no necessary physical validity. The use of such concepts may be very suggestive and stimulating. But even mental operations are subject to certain limitations, and if we transgress these in formulating our tentative concepts we may expect trouble. In particular all mental operations must be made in time, and are therefore ordered in time. Furthermore, no mental operation may assume a knowledge of the future. It can be shown that certain paradoxes arise when these limitations are ignored.

Operational analysis is applicable not only to the meaning of terms or concepts, but to other matters of meaning, as for example, to the meaning of questions. From this point of view I do not know what I mean by a question until I can picture to myself what I would do to check the correctness of an answer which might be presented to me. Analysis of questions from this point of view leads to the recognition that questions can be formulated which allow no possible procedure for checking the correctness of a hypothetical answer. An example is the celebrated question of W. K. Clifford, "Is it possible that as time goes on the dimensions of the universe may be continually changing, but in such a way that we can never detect it, because all our measuring sticks are shrinking in the same way as everything else?" There is no method by which an answer "yes" or "no" to this question could be checked, because by hypothesis, in the question itself, we have ruled out the only method by which the correctness of the answer could be tested. This question must be judged meaningless, therefore. A great many meaningless questions can be formulated, and the clear recognition that meaningless questions are easy to formulate is a great analytical advance.

Not only are there meaningless questions, but many of the problems with which the human intellect has tortured itself turn out to be only "pseudo problems," because they can be formulated only in terms of questions which are meaningless. Many of the traditional problems of philosophy, of religion, or of ethics, are of this character. Consider, for example, the problem of the freedom of the will. You maintain that you are free to take either the right- or the left-hand fork in the road. I defy you to set up a single objective criterion by which you can prove after you have made the turn that you might have made the other. The problem has no meaning in the sphere of objective activity; it only relates to my personal subjective feelings while making the decision.

Continued application of the operational criterion of meaning has proved to be of the greatest assistance in arousing that self-consciousness of what we do in meeting physical situations which is fundamental to criticism.

This book will develop around a few of the simplest possible observations about what we do in dealing with situations. In most cases we shall not endeavor to justify these fundamental observations; it seems to me that they are of such an irreducible simplicity that once stated and apprehended they must command assent. Our main concern will be to examine whether the procedures of our customary practice have sufficiently taken account of these fundamental observations, and if not, how our point of view will be thereby modified. Our analysis will be occupied at the beginning with a rather more elaborate examination of the properties of our mental processes than would perhaps seem to be necessary. My excuse must be that this is the direction in which my own thought seems to have been impelled in the years since publishing my first book. This impulsion has come, I believe, from the realization that only by this sort of analysis can we understand the failure of our former concepts. Furthermore, I believe we will be increasingly driven in this direction in the future by the emphasis of wave mechanics on the observer as a necessary part of any physical system. The rôle of the observer cannot be adequately understood without an appreciation of the way he must think, although it must be admitted that wave mechanics is still a long way from any treatment of this aspect of the observer.

To start as far back as possible, it is obvious that I can never get outside of myself; direct experience embraces only the things in my consciousness—sense impressions of various sorts and various sorts of cerebrations—and naught else. In the material of direct experience I distinguish features which I describe as external to myself and others which I recognize as internal, and possibly there are features where the decision is difficult, as for example whether the pain in my foot is due to a sliver beneath the skin or due to a stone in my shoe. The external features often arouse in me reactions of adjustment of one sort or another, and there are certain conventional devices which I use in making the adjustments. Success in making these adjustments I recognize as desirable, and is something that I strive for, but I do not always attain the success that I could desire.

There is no such thing as public or mass consciousness. In the last analysis science is only my private science, art is my private art, religion my private religion, etc. The fact that in deciding what shall be my private science I find it profitable to consider only those aspects of my direct experience in which my fellow beings act in a particular way cannot obscure the essential fact that it is mine and naught else. "Public Science" is a particular kind of the science of private individuals.

This point of view is directly opposed to one which it has recently become popular to emphasize in critical writings, namely that "science" can refer only to the body of knowledge universally held by competent persons. But that there is something more to it, and that there is no getting away from the central position of the individual I believe anyone can see for himself merely by observing that the individual does not regard the following to be a senseless question: "Under what conditions would you draw the conclusion that everyone in the world except yourself had gone crazy?" It is possible to set up criteria for conditions under which this conclusion would be felt to be inevitable. Granted that every individual finds it desirable for his own purposes to concern himself only with what he observes other competent individuals agree on, nevertheless in the last resort every individual must be his own judge of what he shall accept to be satisfactory evidence of competence in another.

This position, which I suppose is the solipsist position, is often felt to be absurd and contrary to common sense. How, it is asked, can there be agreement as to experience unless there are external things which both you and I perceive? Part of the hostility to the solipsist position is, I think, merely due to confusion of thinking, and there is a strong element of the pseudo-problem mixed up here. If I say that an external thing is merely a part of my direct experience to which I find that you react in certain ways, what more is there to be said, or indeed what other operational meaning can be attached to the concept of an external thing? It seems to me that as I have stated it, the solipsist position, if indeed this be the solipsist position, is a simple statement of what direct observation gives me, and we have got to adjust our thinking so that it will not seem repugnant.

There are two observations on the character of our direct conscious experience which appeal to me as perhaps more fundamental than others. The first is that our experience is composed of activities of one sort or another, that is, that it is not static, but in continual flux. Let one try to imagine what static self-consciousness would be like to convince one-self. The second is that the only possible attitude toward the facts of experience as it unrolls is one of acceptance. In particular, an attitude of acceptance toward the future is the only attitude that one can possibly adopt. Any mental devices that we invent in order to adjust ourselves to our experience must be subject to these restrictions, and if for special purposes we find it convenient to ignore this aspect of experience we must constantly hold in mind that we have a device of only limited applicability. In particular, since there is no means by which we can foresee the future we cannot tell in advance whether any mental device or invention will be successful in meeting new situations, and the only possible way of finding out is to actually try it.

# III. THOUGHT, LANGUAGE

SCIENCE, language, rational thought, are devices by which I try to make adjustments and I have to find by experiment whether these are successful devices. In judging their success I recognize that there are two vitally different sorts of adjustment that I would like to be able to make.

In the first place, I would like to understand the events of the past. The urge to do this may be purely intellectual; this urge to understand nevertheless does seem to have in at least some people the elementality of a primary appetite. In attempting to understand the events of the past, at any particular instant, we are dealing with a closed problem, since there are only a finite number of elements to deal with, and success in making our adjustment is conceivable, and any proposed solution may be adequately tested. As a matter of fact I suppose that success even with this closed problem will never be complete, but that we will always have to put up with solutions that are satisfactory only from certain limited points of view.

In the second place, our face may be set toward the future, and we may want some method of predicting the future or at least making adequate preparation for it. The method which we employ in reaching for this second objective is essentially the same as in reaching for the first, not because we do not recognize that another method would be desirable in solving a totally different problem, but because it is obvious that we have absolutely no other means of preparing for the future except on the basis of what has already happened to us. One can convince oneself of this by trying to give operational meaning to the question whether there may not be some other method of preparing for the future than on the basis of past experience. We are caught then, and can do nothing else. It is fortunate that past experience has shown that whenever in the past we were able to understand our then past experience we could on the basis of it look a certain distance into the future.

Thus although the method of our adjustment when we try to prepare for the future may be the same as when we try only to understand the past, the problem is now no longer a closed one, and we must be continually prepared to find that our solutions are only partially successful, and we must continually check our solutions by their success in predicting.

We now inquire how far our inventions for making adjustments recognize these fundamental requirements, and therefore to what extent we may expect success as complete as possible in meeting all the situations of experience.

I suppose that the fundamental human invention is language, and that we owe the progress of the race to it more than to anything else. Without language we could not communicate with each other and thus ensure that my private science has those desirable properties which I call public science, nor could I probably even engage in some of the more abstract forms of thought.

The first observation about language is that the language with which we describe a given happening is not uniquely determined by the happening itself, but our choice of language depends on the particular aspect which is of immediate interest. In particular, there are ways of using language that correspond more closely to the fundamental fact that our experience is a string of activities than do other methods. For example, to say "I see a horse" gets recognizably closer to the direct experience than to say "There is a horse," for the first describes my experience as an activity, whereas the second freezes the activity and substitutes for it something static, something which did not occur in direct experience, and something which itself constitutes a human invention, and is so far questionable.

It requires perhaps a certain amount of sophistication to feel the difference between the two methods of expressing experience, but on reflection it is evident that the second mode of expression lays emphasis on the postulate, or the invention, of a "thing," existing for itself, outside me, and this static thing is one remove at least from direct experience. But the first mode of expression may be seen to contain also the same construction, for what is the meaning of the "horse" which it uses. It is only that the constructional aspect is here less insistent. It would appear then that every noun in language involves a certain amount of construction and abstraction. We do not experience *things; things* are a construction of ours the function of which is to emphasize the resemblance between aspects of our present immediate experience and aspects of our past experience, something which it proves enormously useful to do. But if nouns involve an element of construction and are at least one remove from direct experience, how is it with verbs? These are apparently a direct expression of activity and may therefore be expected to reproduce direct experience with greater fidelity. But on consideration one sees that not only is our experience a string of activities, but it is a string of specific activities never recurrent, whereas verbs are applicable to classes of activity, and therefore involve an element of abstraction. To call my act of eating breakfast this morning the same as my act of eating it yesterday is obviously an approximation, not corresponding exactly to experience. Thus the invention of verbs has something very much in common with the invention of nouns; in both cases we analyze our memories into little bundles which are so similar that it is useful to associate an identity with them and think of them as recurrent. Nouns refer to the more passive and permanent aspects of our consciousness, whereas verbs refer to more active aspects, with which are associated volition, and in which the element of flux is more immediately obvious. But in either case we are dealing with a construction which does not reproduce experience with fidelity, but only certain features of it.

If then, language does not reproduce experience with fidelity, to what does it owe its success in dealing with experience? It seems to me that it owes whatever success it attains to its ability to set up and maintain certain correspondences with experience. Why it is that we are able to set up these correspondences and particularly to maintain them, is I think a meaningless question: we can only accept our ability to do so as a brute fact. The operational meaning of the concept of "thing" involves merely a description of the fact that it is possible to maintain such correspondences.

It does have meaning, however, to inquire what the details of the process are by which I set up the correspondence in any special case. What do I do, for example, in assuring myself that I correlate with the word "apple" the aspect of experience that you wish me to correlate? You may if you like give me a definition of apple as a fruit with certain properties, but if I try to assure myself that I have made the proper correspondence for "fruit" and for the other terms of the definition, I will presently find myself back at the starting point. It is well known that there have to be certain undefined terms in any such inquiry as this.

Or take another example that emphasizes the point particularly well. How shall I set up the correspondence between the words "left-handed screw" and the object you wish me to envisage? A few trials will be sufficient, I think, to show that it is impossible to define "left-handed screw" in words such that intuitive knowledge of something equivalent to a left-handed screw (for example, a knowledge of the points of the compass and up and down) is not involved somewhere. In other words, it is fundamentally impossible to define left-handed screw in language alone, but all that we can do is to point to one as an example. The method of setting up the correspondence between the words and object "left-handed screw" cannot be specified in words. In general, the processes of establishing the correspondences through which language has meaning cannot themselves be described in language, but involve getting outside the system of language. The processes can only be learning by observation, use, and verification. No language can give a complete account of any situation of experience in the sense that given only the language we can reproduce the situation. This restriction is not usually prominent, but it may be painfully evident, for example, to an archeologist endeavoring to decipher the hieroglyphics of Central America. It is most important to recognize the existence of this limitation if we are going to realize clearly the essential limitations of what we may do with language.

Thought itself is subject to similar restrictions. Although I may not be able to describe in words the process of setting up the correspondence between the words "left-handed screw" and the object, I may be able to assure myself that the correspondence has been made by means of certain intuitively accepted motor sensations. But to assure myself that these motor sensations are correctly used involves the recognition of the motor sensation when it recurs, and to assure myself that I am correctly remembering the motor sensation will involve something different, and so back in never ending regression. That is, as long as thought involves bits of identified remembering, and it seems to me that any thought I am willing to call rational involves as much as this, it will be impossible to give a complete account of what happens within the system of thought itself; that is, thought is essentially incapable of completeness.

Going back to the question of language, it would seem to me that it is the merest truism, to be admitted as soon as we have achieved even the most rudimentary freshness of perception, that the structure of language and of experience are not the same. Yet it appears to be the fashion at present in some quarters to insist on the similarity of structure of language and experience. It has always been a major bewilderment to me to understand how anyone can experience such a commonplace event as an automobile going up the street and seriously maintain that there is identity of structure of this continually flowing, dissolving and reforming thing, and the language that attempts to reproduce it with discrete units, tied together by remembered conventions. Those analyses which stress the similarity of structure and language and experience point out that the only *reason* why language can successfully deal with experience is that it has the same structure. This I suspect is rather the concealed reason why similarity of structure is ascribed to language and experience, because it is felt that no other explanation of the success of language in dealing with experience is conceivable.

But is it really an explanation of success to point out the similarity of structure? I suppose that the idea is that experience consists of parts and language consists of parts; language is used in dealing with experience by setting up a correspondence between the parts of language and the parts of experience, and the fact that the correspondence can be set up means identity of structure. We may, if we like, say that by definition the systems have the same structures if it is possible to establish correspondences between the two systems. But this is largely a matter of words, and unprofitable. What we usually understand by similarity of structure involves the ability to set up a complete, not a partial, set of correspondences. The impossibility of setting up a complete correspondence is obvious without discussion, or if we wish a formal proof, we have it in our analysis of the methods by which the correspondences are set up, which we saw cannot be described in language itself, but are something that we learn by the doing of them or by seeing them done. Of course we are here ruling out purely physical "explanations" of the method of establishing correspondences in terms of the structure of the brain, such as the psychologist may be able to give us some day, but as stated in the beginning, our discussion is entirely of things in consciousness.

In connection with the feeling that an explanation is required for such success as language attains, it must be remembered that it is not just language which deals successfully with experience, but language plus me; language is something which *I* use, and without me is merely sounding brass and a tinkling cymbal. And if language did not deal successfully with experience, would I not continue to strive until I found something that did, or going still further, is not language by definition merely a certain part of my device for dealing with experience? The fact that this involves communication with my fellow beings is merely a reflection of the fact that I am a social creature, and a very large and insistent part of my experience demands putting myself into correct relations with my fellows. All this need not diminish our admiration for the success of this human device, or if we are still capable of the emotion of wonder we may get as much kick out of the spectacle of mankind getting into moderately successful contact with the enormous complexities of its experience by this invention as we may from a contemplation of the galaxies of the night sky.

The more one thinks of it the more unlike do the structures of language and experience appear. Complete similarity of structure would demand a one to one correspondence. This we obviously do not have; not only is it impossible to get all the aspects of experience into language, but language does not afford a unique method of reporting any isolated aspect of experience, and further, nothing is easier than to set up combinations of language that have no correspondence in experience. Linguistic structures of all sorts are possible, governed by all sorts of rules or by no rules at all. Some may be constructed according to the principles of logic, as for example, the various non-Euclidean geometries, about which all that can be said is that as a matter of brute fact they do not correspond with the geometry of real objects, or others may be the most hopeless jumble of incongruous elements, as most of our political and social thinking. The mere fact that such structures are possible should be sufficient to show that the structure of language is not the same as that of direct experience.

One reason that such complicated structures enter into language is that we want to be able to use language to express in the first place physical experiences, then sentiments aroused by the experiences, then the sentiments aroused by those sentiments and so on in never-ending sequence. Presently we become confused by the complexity of the situation, and make the wrong correspondences between language and what we are thinking about, so that ultimately a particular bit of language may have no other significance than that it happened to have been the end product of a particular bit of cerebration.

It seems to me that all we can say is that we recognize certain features in experience, and there are certain features in language, and that we can set up and maintain an approximate correspondence between some of these features. But nothing could be further from the truth than that there is *complete* correspondence of structure between all experience and all language, or even between any limited aspects of language and experience.

An essential distinction between language and experience is that language separates out from the living matrix little bundles and freezes them; in doing this it produces something totally unlike experience, but nevertheless useful. That is, language as language is divorced from the *activity* which is the basal property of all our experience. Although language has this essential characteristic, nevertheless *language used* is obviously an activity, and as an activity may reacquire some of those properties of continuous flux and change which as language proper it sought to divest itself of. Strictly speaking, the connotation of the same words can never be twice the same, but connotation is continually being slightly altered as the living matrix in which it is embedded alters. Because of this aspect of language, namely that language must be *language used,* language is doomed to an only partial success in its fundamental task of analyzing experience into fixed aspects with identity which recur, and it must always suffer from a certain blurring and indistinctness of outline. Examples of the havoc which may result from shifting meanings and connotations may be found in many of the paradoxes; in most of the situations of daily life we have learned to avoid such dilemmas instinctively, but I think we would find it impossible to give a rationally satisfying analysis of exactly what we do in sidestepping such dilemmas.

Too great facility in finding the words to express all one's experiences and ideas involves, I believe, a particular danger. For success in making a sufficiently good analysis of experience into static bits may easily lead to the belief that experience is actually composed of such static bits (as some intuitionist geometers have supposed that a line is composed of points), and this in turn may lead to the belief that a satisfactory verbal analysis, when once found, is the unique and complete expression of the whole situation.

Language thus appears to have inherent limitations, and we shall later trace to them some of our difficulties in making perfect connection with experience. Suppose now, that instead of demanding that my science be a "public science," that is, a "communicated science," I should content myself with an uncommunicated science, which I could of course rigorously check by applying it to concrete physical situations, could I thereby escape the dangers which appear to be inherent in the use of language? This would demand, of course, that my own thinking would have to be conducted without the verbal element of language. One may, with considerable justification, take the view that language is more than merely verbal. However, it is not necessary to argue this point, since it is purely a matter of formal definition, but merely inquire whether non-verbal thought can avoid the pitfalls which we have seen above to be inherent in language.

In the first place I suppose it will be universally conceded that modes of thought and reasoning are possible from which the verbal element is almost entirely absent. Perhaps one of the best examples of such non-verbal thought is afforded by what we do when we analyze the action of a machine, or sketch on paper the design for a piece of apparatus. What I do in designing an apparatus is to reproduce in imagination what my activities would be in watching the performance of the complete apparatus, and I know that for me such an experience is almost entirely motor in character. I see one part pushing another and have a tactile feeling for the forces and a kinetic appreciation of the resulting motion, all without consciously getting onto the verbal level. If I analyze what happens I think that I instinctively recognize that a certain kind of push or pull will be followed by a certain kind of motion because I remember past situations which aroused in me the same reactions, and I know what happened in those cases. Thus it seems to me that any dealing with the situation at all involves tying up into bundles, and recognizing them when they recur, of little bits of past experience which have proved to be of significance. This tying up of experience into bundles which are capable of recognition appears to me to be the primary tool of self-conscious rational thought, whether or not it gets through to the verbal level, where the bundle may be associated with a noun or verb or other part of speech. In this respect thought itself cannot have the same structure as experience and we must not expect complete success in dealing with all the aspects of experience.

The structure of thought is thus palpably not the same as the structure of experience, but it is obviously very close to the structure of language (in the future in order to be more specific I shall understand by language only verbal language), and for many purposes it is perhaps safe to use the two interchangeably. But the two are not identical; thought is infinitely the richer, for it may contain an awareness of the continually shifting background of connotation that is incapable of expression in language. Since thought is thus closer to experience than language, we may expect language to get us into some difficulties that can be avoided by a keen enough analysis, but until other intrinsically different and at present unconceived modes of thought are devised, we may expect certain limitations that we cannot surmount imposed by the failure of thought to reproduce exactly the quality of experience.

It is, I think, obvious that not all the mental processes which are involved in rational thought get up to the level of consciousness. Examples of such processes are the processes by which I recognize the identity of an act or thing when it recurs in experience, or the method by which I associate words with certain images. Since such processes do not get into consciousness, they are incapable of analysis by conscious thought and must be accepted as ultimates; it must be sufficient for me that I can do certain kinds of things. Because I cannot analyze the act of recognition, for example, into component parts separately performed, it is meaningless to attempt to find the operational significance of recognition. (This, of course, is all from the point of view of direct apprehension in consciousness; the psychologist gives other meanings to these questions and may analyze them by other methods.)

We have by no means exhausted the necessary limitations of thought in pointing out that it blurs the activity aspect of experience. There seem to be various urges which it is very difficult to resist, and which may perhaps be results of intrinsic properties of our thinking apparatus, which we nevertheless recognize are not suitable guides to conduct. An example of such is our insistence on a first cause, and our simultaneous recognition that any cause which we might accept as the first must itself have had a cause. Or our instinctive feeling that time must have a beginning, and our inability when we get there to conceive of a moment without a preceding moment. Or there is another sort of thing in our insistent attempt to visualize death as some sort of experience, set against our intellectual realization that death is not experience. I suppose that our inability to think of death except in terms of experience has had more social consequences than any other vagary of the human mind.

The inability of our minds to transcend experience in certain respects may easily involve us in misapprehensions. An example is the popular reaction to the suggestion of general relativity theory that space may be finite. This statement, of purely mathematical significance, is misapprehended, and its meaning thought to involve a finite end of space, like the end of a dark corridor. The mind is incapable of visualizing a blank wall surrounding space; if we did find ourselves in the presence of such a limitation we imagine that we would think of the wall itself as existing in an extension of space. Because we are incapable of visualizing what a thing would mean in terms of experience, we reject the whole notion as contrary to common sense and absurd.

Of course the common-sense view has elements of truth in it; what the common-sense view is really doing is to point out that the conceptual space of our ordinary experience cannot be bounded by a wall. If any such experience did present itself, a more satisfactory way of describing the experience would be to say that our ordinary concept of space had ceased to be applicable; it would be a matter of words whether we would find it advantageous to extend our previous concept of space to include the new phenomena, or whether we would prefer to reserve the old concept of space for the old phenomena and coin a new word to correspond to the enlarged experience.

The process by which we would attempt to deal with an entirely novel experience, for of course we would have to accept the experience and attempt to deal with it in some fashion, would, I suppose, be at first a process of successive approximations. We would start by applying the older concept until it got us into trouble; after it had got us into trouble often enough we would begin to find some sort of regularity in the way in which the trouble occurred, just exactly like a rat trying to get out of a maze and running his nose into the end of a blank passage, and we would then formulate a set of verbal rules, instructing us at a certain stage of operations to switch our procedure and begin operating in a new way which we had found appropriate by the method of trial and error. After we had operated in this way many times, the whole complex, old procedure, trouble, switch, new rules, would form itself as a new and integrated whole in our minds, and we would presently find ourselves meeting the situation instinctively without any conscious analysis into parts, exactly like the rat after he has learned the maze. This it seems to me is typical of much of scientific theory building; the end product is a unit, expressed in terms of integrated concepts involving the complicated operations by which the complete situation is dealt with. But such integrated concepts are not necessary in order to meet successfully the situation, which we could do from the moment that we were able to formulate verbally our rules for switching from one procedure to the other. Such integrated rules are merely devices of convenience, increasing enormously our ease and speed in dealing with the situation.

One of the aspects in which our method of thinking most obviously fails to correspond exactly to experience I believe to be in our concept of time, especially its expression in mathematical form, which affects all our scientific theorizing. The time of the mathematician is a one-dimensional continuum, reaching forward and backward to plus and minus infinity, everywhere homogeneous, and with an orgin which may be situated arbitrarily. The time of the mathematician seems to have got itself ineradicably embedded in the thinking of modern civilization, for apparently we all nearly always think of time as a homogeneous and unlimited one-dimensional sequence, all past time on one side, all future time on the other, separated by the present which is in continuous motion from past to future. What could be more unlike the time of experience, apprehended with true freshness, which consists of a blurred sequence of memories, culminating in the budding and unfolding present? An integral component of this budding and unfolding present is an attitude of expectancy toward the future, which we shall accept without cavil or argument, no matter what it brings. The instinctive urge of our minds to believe in a future causally determined by the past is obviously opposed to our simultaneous recognition that the future can only be accepted no matter how it breaks with the past, and is just another example of the incompatibility of some of our strongest mental impulses. This conflict contains the seeds of trouble. In this case there seems to me no doubt but that the attitude of acceptance of the future must always have the right of way over the other. The recognition that the only possible attitude toward the future is one of unreserved acceptance, no matter how distasteful or contrary to expectations, is fundamental to all sane thinking.

But the time of the mathematician, or of most of our thought, has no such unique apex, with its immanent possibility that everything may go awry. Our habitual thought almost always disregards this aspect, we recognize it only when forced to, and we deal with it even yet only as a second approximation, by formulating a special set of rules, not integrated with the rules we use in most of our thinking. It seems to me that our failure to recognize sufficiently vividly this very vital aspect in which our ordinary thinking fails to reproduce experience with complete fidelity is at the bottom of some of our fundamental troubles in mathematics and its applications. From the point of view of operations the time of the mathematician is merely the time of memory. The time of memory has the property that we may imagine ourselves situated at any point of it and from that point our recollections may range in either direction backward or forward, provided only that they do not touch the present. But this is a dead time, divested of the living hazard of the present, and when the mathematician uses this time he can give an account only of the dead. Our consciousness of this vital limitation must not be dulled by the enormous effectiveness of the mathematical concept of time in dealing with the situations of past experience, nor must we on the other hand think that the mathematician's concept of time is capable of dealing with all the questions that we may put. I suspect that if it had been vividly realized that the time of experience is not homogeneous backward and forward, unlike the time of the mathematician, a certain very eminent speculator would not have sought in the structure of mathematical time an explanation of the fact that "time's arrow" always points forward. Whether the question as to why it is that time moves forward can be given meaning in terms of any possible concept of time may well be open to doubt, but it certainly cannot be given meaning in terms of the dead time of the mathematician. This must be accepted as one of the unanalyzables.

Neither do I see how one can speak of a possible "quantization" of time, as is not infrequently done. If one asks what one does to determine whether time is quantized one thinks of time as coming in little measurable bundles, so that perhaps the mathematical parameter which gives the time can take on only integral values, but if one asks how large the bundles are, or what determines where one bundle ends and the next begins, or what determines when time jumps from one integral value to another, one can think only of a quantized time embedded in a background of ordinary time. Or in other words, the notion of quantized time is inconsistent with the notion of time as we experience it. The only meaning which I can see in the term "quantized time" is a recognition of the possibility that there may be situations to which our present concept of time will prove to be inapplicable, but it seems to me impossible to describe the failure of the present concept in terms of the present concept.

The method of successive approximations which we adopt in using our ordinary concept of time for dealing with experience consists essentially in the analysis which we have just given; we recognize that the ordinary concept does not quite fit, that it may be expected to fail in certain situations, when we must apply other sorts of consideration, and the complex of original concept and analysis constitutes exactly our enlarged set of rules by which we make the next approximation to complete success.

Possibly our intuitive feeling for the nature of time might have been different if we had been presented in youth with some vivid figure in terms of which to think. The Greeks must have had a different feeling for time than we. We usually think of the future as stretching before us, and ourselves as going to meet it. Who knows how much this picture may be responsible for the feeling of moderns that the future has "existence" and is essentially predictable, or was it that this feeling for the future developed after our belief in the predictability of the future was established by the growth of modern science? The Greek, on the other hand, thought of himself as facing the past, with the future behind him, coming up over his shoulder as the landscape unfolds to one riding back to the engine. Even this picture did not get rid of the idea of the "existence" of the future, but it did emphasize that the future is unknown. If some one could invent a figure for speaking of the flight of time, in which the idea is prominent that in our thought we recognize that the germinating present contains the seeds of a complete break with the past, he might alter the future course of thinking.

# IV. LOGIC

WITH this brief analysis of our fundamental conscious activities of thought and language, with its recognition that these are the tools used in meeting the situations of experience, and that as tools they do not do everything that we would like to have them, but have certain imperfections and limitations, let us pass on to an examination of the complex structures which thought and language erect in trying to reduce experience to understandability. Theoretical physics is coming to depend largely on mathematics, and mathematics in its turn rests on logic, and in fact is sometimes said to be merely a branch of logic. Let us begin, therefore, by inquiring into the operational background of logic.

Extravagant claims are sometimes made for logic, and these claims sometimes even appear in the definition of logic; thus there is the definition of Bertrand Russell of logic as the science which draws *necessary* conclusions. This is but an example of a very common tendency to set logic off from the other activities of the human intellect by the certainty of its conclusions. These conclusions are felt to be invested with an absolute certainty, so that in fact they *could not be otherwise*. What do we mean by absolute certainty; how shall we recognize it when we see it, or what test shall we apply to assure ourselves that some conclusion which purports to have absolute certainty really has it?

One very obvious comment can be made at the beginning; any test that is applied is applied by me, either in person or vicariously, and part of the process of applying the test consists in my assuring myself that I am applying the test properly. A test consists in following a certain set of rules or a pattern of procedure; how may I be sure that I have not deviated from the rule or the prescribed pattern? I, who am applying the rules, am myself a thing that makes mistakes, and whose activities have to be checked. How shall I be sure that I have not been the subject of an illusion, and that although I thought I was correctly applying the rule, I really was not? What assurance have I that I did not go insane during the application of the rule and recover my sanity later? It seems to me that there can be no answer to questionings of this sort that do not involve somewhere an element of circularity, and that there can be no rigorous defense against the suspicion of insanity. All we have are procedures which we recognize as having a certain probability of correctness—absolute certainty and a water-tight logic are equally chimeras. Logic is a game which we cannot even begin to play unless we make tacit assumptions which cannot be checked in practice.

Assuming that we are willing to play the game as expected, and that I can know when I am doing as the rules demand, let us examine some of the things we do in applying logic to any concrete situation.

Induction and deduction are recognized to be fundamental logical processes; precisely what is involved in these? What is the meaning of the general principles which I obtain by induction, and how may I know that I apply these principles correctly in any special case?

If we answer operationally our question as to what a general principle is by examining what we do with it, we see that it is a rule of procedure which we accept as a valid guide for conduct in cases beyond our present experience. If we ask how we can be sure that there are such guides, the answer must be that we can never be sure until we have tried, in view of our recognition that the future is not bound by the past. The contrary feeling, which is so common, that there *are* eternal principles, which afford a secure basis for conduct, can have no justification as a description of anything that actually happens to us.

The operational statement is something like this: it would be convenient to have compact rules of conduct to guide me and to save mental effort in the face of new situations. I find that I can formulate compact rules that apply to all cases of my remembered experience; I shall therefore adopt these rules as a guide to future conduct. The process of getting out of the rule the instructions as to how to act in new and specific cases is called deduction in those cases where the rule is so drawn that the instructions may be obtained by the methods of logic. The fact that the instructions may be so obtained is no accident, because that was the way the rule was made. The process by which the rule is formulated is induction. It seems to me that induction involves first a clear recognition of the requirements which any rule must have in order to be acceptable, and then a more or less inspired guess at such an actual formulation. In our guessing, the hypothesis that we are on a fruitful tack, and will be able eventually to deliver what we want is often very helpful.

Induction and deduction are thus simply a game which we play with ourselves; I am looking for rules with certain properties: I know that certain types of rule are excluded: I seize on one that seems to have none of the objections, and which I agree to handle as if it had the desired properties. Then in any specific new case this rule gives me certain instructions as to what I shall do, and these instructions must be correct provided my hypothesis was sound that I had hit on a suitable rule. The whole procedure contains an inescapable element of circularity, and cannot be justified by any process in the realm of logic itself. The only justification is convenience as shown by experience, but in the back of the heads of most people there is a metaphysical argument to the effect that principles do exist, and the universe is run according to them, and if one is only intelligent enough he may discover them.

Operationally, a general principle can never contain any-thing intrinsically new, and the syllogism is merely a con-cealed tautology. Consider, for example, the classical form: all men are mortal, Socrates is a man, therefore Socrates is mortal. If I ask how I am sure operationally that the major premise is correct, that is, how do I know that all men really are mortal, the only answer can be that I know because I have verified by observation that all men are mortal, in which case I have already verified that Socrates is mortal. The justifica-tion for the syllogism must be sought in something else than its ability to reveal fresh truth. It does have a very great social justification, because my fellow man can hand to me an enormous amount of his own experience wrapped up into the compact form of a general principle, and then I can unravel from this general principle an enormous amount of detail by operating on the statement according to certain rules. The use is not only social, for I can wrap up for myself in easily remembered form for future use an enormous amount of material in the form of a general principle which otherwise might escape me.

There is one particular rule of logic which has been often quoted and much discussed lately, the so-called law of the excluded middle, which is often stated in the form: a thing is either $A$ or it is not-$A$. Operationally, if this statement is to have real content and not be merely a concealed tautology, it must imply something like the following: I am given a certain object to examine; if it has the property $A$ then I shall find that certain operations performed on it give certain results; similarly if it has the property not-$A$ then I shall find that certain other operations performed on it give certain other results. The law of the excluded middle makes the statement that if I operate according to the one or the other of these two rules of operation, then I shall find that one or the other of the operations has yielded a positive result.

Obviously as a general statement about any two sets of operations this is going much too far, and the statement can be correct only in virtue of some special connection between the operation used to test for $A$ and for not-$A$. Is such a special connection possible? We can easily see one way in which there might be such a special connection. If the second test by definition consists in observing the result of the first test, and if a positive result for the second test by definition consists in the observation of a failure of the first test, then we have accomplished what we want, provided that the first test is so constructed that when it does not give a positive result it "fails." In such a case, however, we have reduced the whole matter to a tautology.

It is, I think, an instinctive recognition of the usually tautological character of the law of the excluded middle, without, however, a sufficiently far-reaching analysis to show exactly the place where the tautology enters, that leads many people to regard the law as a necessary "law of thought," and the contrary to be unthinkable.

If we are not willing to descend to tautology, it is not easy to set up rules for $A$ and not-$A$ so related that they shall automatically ensure the correctness of the law of the excluded middle. Even when we are willing to admit the tautology, we have come perilously close to begging the question in our procedure above, for we had to assume that the first test was so constructed that it gave either a positive result, or else it failed, and this smells suspiciously like the law of the excluded middle come home to roost. In considering whether tests can be constructed which satisfy these demands, we have to distinguish different classes of objects to which the test might be applicable.

Consider first tests applicable to physical objects. Can I make my test for example in such a way as to justify me in saying an apple is either green or it is not green? The operational situation is obvious enough. There must be some sort of test which I can apply to any particular apple with which I may be presented. This test may perhaps be a test performed with physical instruments, as for example, I may say that by definition the apple is green if the center of gravity of the reflected light has a wave length between 5200Å and 5600Å. The question now is, is this test such that we can always assert that the apple either satisfies it or it does not? It is obvious that it is not of this kind, since we know that because of instrumental uncertainty and errors of observation cases will arise in which we cannot say whether the wave length is greater or less than one of the critical values. This it seems to me is characteristic of most judgments involving physical processes—the law of the excluded middle is not a valid description of our actual physical experience—there has to be a third category of doubtful, in addition to positive or negative.

There is another class of statement to which the law obviously does not apply, as for example, "virtue is either green or it is not green." The difficulty here is obvious—the concept of green does not apply to virtue for the simple reason that there is no operation by which I can decide whether virtue is green or not—the concept is not applicable, and the statement "virtue is green" is meaningless. Neither can a meaning be assigned to not-green in this case, unless I want to define the property not-green as applying in all those cases where the concept green does not fit, and if one does this, one is back at a tautology or an evasion. It seems much better in this case merely to say that there are properties which it is meaningless to attempt to ascribe to certain classes of things, and that we simply cannot talk about the law of the excluded middle in such cases.

If the law of the excluded middle is to be valid, at all, apparently the realm of validity must be restricted to mental constructs and mental operations—to things we say or think rather than things we do with our hands, for the latter always have a margin of fuzziness which defeats us. Our mental constructions do often appear to have the necessary sharpness —no one doubts that it is legitimate to say "any integer is even or it is not even (odd by definition)."

What other sorts of mental constructions are there with sufficient sharpness, and how may we recognize them in advance? Consider, for example, the concept of truth; is this concept always applicable to statements, and may I say "a statement is either true or it is not true (false by definition)"? This is a particularly important example of the law of the excluded middle, and in fact some people understand just this statement as a statement of the law. What sort of test do I apply in deciding whether a given statement is true or not, and can this test always be applied? In particular, let us suppose that our statement is of a tentative general principle. The operations which I use in determining the truth of general principles have certain curious properties. A general principle by definition is a correct description of *any* case; if I can find a single case in which it is not correct, then by definition it is not a general principle, and I have proved that the principle is not true. But how can I show that it is correct in any case? If I am dealing with a closed class of objects, then I may hope to apply the test to all the members of the class, and thus find by experiment, by the method of exhaustion, whether the principle is true or not. But if the class of objects is open, or infinite, then I cannot hope to apply the method of exhaustion and "true" loses its original operational meaning; I may, however, hope to show that the principle is not true, by finding a specific example to which it does not apply. Hence my statement that the "principle is either true or false" is a false statement because it does not correspond to what is operationally possible in the case. There may, however, be an exception; if it happens that the definition which determines the members of the infinite class is so framed that it automatically rules out any member which does not satisfy the principle, then I may say that the law of the excluded middle does apply in this case because I know in particular that the principle is true for any member of this infinite class. This method would also apply to a closed class of objects, provided the definition of the numbers of the class was properly framed. For finite classes "truth" may have two operationally distinct meanings, which are equivalent. Only one of these meanings is possible for an infinite class. Hence all the implications of "truth" are not the same in the two cases and operationally, truth is a complex concept. Yet we usually make no distinction, and cover all meanings with a single word.

There is another interesting point here. By what method shall I show that the definition of the members of the infinite class has been so framed as to rule out automatically any member not having the property in question? It may not be obvious from the definition itself, but the proof may involve a process of logical deduction, using various devices of logic, as perhaps the principle of contradiction, which consists in showing that if the converse property is assumed a contradiction is involved. As an example, consider the infinite class of the odd numbers. These all have the property that their square is odd, but this requires proof and is not contained in the definition of the class. The law of the excluded middle obviously applies to this situation, for when we know that a certain statement is true of all members of a class, we can obviously say the statement is either true or false, knowing it to be true.

But what shall we do in cases that are not so obvious, where the deduction of the property from the definition is not so easy, and in fact so difficult that we are not yet able to make it? An example is afforded by the classical query of Brouwer, which has provoked so much discussion among mathematicians. Brouwer's example may be thrown into the following form. I make the statement, "Somewhere in the decimal expansion of $\pi$ there occurs the sequence of digits 0123456789." Then may I say, "This statement is either true or false"? It would be known to be true if I could exhibit the place in the expansion where the sequence occurs. But this neither I nor anyone else can do. Or it would be false if I could show that the assumption that the sequence does occur at some definite place leads to contradiction. But this again has not been done. Hence the operational statement of the situation must be that since neither of the procedures by which the truth or falsity of the statement might be proved can be applied, the concept of truth is simply not applicable in this case, and the statement is meaningless.

But this conclusion will appear to many highly unsatisfactory; they immediately ask, but how do you know that some day it will not be possible either to exhibit the place in the expansion where the sequence occurs, or else to show that the assumption that there is such a place must lead to contradiction? To which I would reply that of course I do not know that some day such a proof will not be given, and that when the proof is given the statement ceases to be meaningless, and becomes either true or false.

This conclusion will doubtless appear even more unsatisfactory, because it exhibits truth as something not absolute, but in this case as depending on the degree of development of human skill in mathematics. But this it seems to me is no more than a statement of the actual situation—meanings are determined by operations—operations are performed by human beings in time and are subject to the essential limitations of the time of our experience—the full meaning of any term involves the addition of a date—future operations mean nothing except as they are described in terms of operations performed now. Because of the fundamental properties of activity itself, truth can have no such static, absolute, meaning as we would like to give it.

Or the situation may be described in another way; our endeavor was to frame such a concept, "truth," that it would be applicable to any statement whatever. This involves finding a set of operations applicable to all statements—such a set of operations is proposed, and we find by experiment that it is not applicable to certain statements that can be made about infinite classes. This means merely that we were not completely successful in framing our concept, and we may well wonder whether our original ideal was possible of attainment.

The reason that our proposed operation failed to be applicable to the infinite class was that here it encountered limitations imposed by the temporal character of all activity, so that if we had seen far enough ahead we would not have anticipated success in the beginning. If we are well advised we will endeavor to frame concepts which recognize the various essential limitations, and we can expect success only when we thus recognize such limitations. But even when the fundamental limitations are properly recognized in the beginning I believe that in general complete success is very seldom attained; I have seen no criterion by which one can tell in advance whether complete success is possible or not, so that I believe we must always be prepared for partial failure.

Other implications of the operational meaning of truth are well brought out by another somewhat different example. A number is algebraic if it is the root of a certain type of algebraic equation, and it is defined to be transcendental if it is not the root of such an equation. Obviously, since not all algebraic equations and all their roots can be written down, the only method of proving that any particular num-

ber is transcendental is to show that the assumption that it
may be expressed as the root of such an equation leads to
contradiction. This proof is usually very difficult to give; there
is no general method known, but special methods have to
be devised for dealing with special cases, and very few numbers are actually known to be transcendental. The proof
that π is transcendental was given in 1882. In 1881 was this a
true statement "π is either transcendental or it is not"? The
operational position must be that this was not a true statement in 1881, but that it did become true in 1882. For not only
was it not known in 1881 how to show that π was either
transcendental or not, but it was not even known whether
the assumption of the possibility of showing this would lead
to contradiction or not. The jealous mathematician will
doubtless retort to this position that of course it makes no
difference to π whether you have proved something about it
or not, and that it was as a matter of fact just as transcendental
in 1881 as in 1882.

This position involves the thesis that things have properties
fixed and inherent, independent of anything that we may
do about it. This is merely an aspect of the trait of all thought
of endeavoring to analyze experience into little frozen bits,
and neglects the consideration that experience is essentially
activity. "Property" is an invented concept, defined itself
by the property that things have properties in and of themselves, independent of what we do or think. But it is always
dangerous to define concepts by their properties, and in this
case we have obviously attempted the impossible, for we have
neglected to remember that "property" must find its meaning
in operations, and that these operations are performed by
some one, so that it is meaningless to talk about the thing in
itself, for we always have the system of operator and operand.
That is, here again is an example in which we have failed
of complete success in inventing the kind of concept we

wanted to invent because we failed to take into account an inherent limitation.

The bearing of all this discussion of the meaning of truth on the law of the excluded middle must, I think, be obvious. Even when we restrict ourselves to mental objects and mental operations we can expect to find no general method by which we can tell in advance whether the law is applicable or not. There are cases in which the only method is the method of experimentation—examination of all conceivable implications. The most that we can hope to attain by such experimental examination is a proof that the law is not applicable. Pythagoras might have thought that he was justified in saying "a statement is either true or false." He would have been wrong in this idea, but his error did not become demonstrable until infinite classes were invented. Similarly, there may be other concepts to which we think the law of the excluded middle may be applicable, but exceptional cases may be found later.

Let us go back to our original typical syllogism "All men are mortal, Socrates is a man—Socrates is mortal." What is the nature of the operations we apply in thought in trying to convince ourselves that this is a valid statement? I suppose that various more or less pictorial devices are used by different persons in doing this; the device of drawing on paper closed regions to represent the various classes of object involved is a very convenient method. But whatever method is adopted will be found, I think, to involve handling the various members of the syllogism like the things of ordinary experience—like the counters of a game which can be moved about preserving their identity. That is, logic as an enterprise presupposes an analysis into fixed things and terms with fixed meanings. If the meaning of the terms changes from one end of the syllogism to the other, we can have no confidence that it is giving the correct result. But we have seen that the analysis of experience into things or recurrent activities that can be tagged with a name is only an approximate reproduction of experience. Logic at best, therefore, can only be approximately applicable to experience, and its conclusions can have certainly no more validity in application than our analysis of experience into fixed and recurrent bits. If one asks by what process one may be sure that one's terms do have sufficient fixity of significance to serve as the terms of a syllogism, I believe that the answer is that much experience has given one an instinctive feeling for "sufficient" fixity; this on analysis will be found to involve a great deal of experimentation in doubtful cases, so that ultimately an element of circularity is involved, and all we can eventually say is that the term has sufficient fixity to be used in a syllogism if it works that way. Of course the process by which one assures oneself that the syllogism is stating an accurate result in any special case cannot itself be described in terms of logical processes.

Here then is an additional reason why a syllogism or any rule of logic such as the law of the excluded middle, may not be valid; not only may the operations presupposed in the particular case not be applicable, but the terms used may not have sufficient fixity of meaning. Although the mental objects of ordinary experience doubtless do have sufficient fixity, it is easy to set up special linguistic structures whose meaning is not fixed, but fluent, dependent on the connotation of what has gone before. When one attempts to practise logic with such terms, one may expect to come to grief. Many paradoxes may be shown to involve the use of terms with fluent meanings, and in my paper on Mengenlehre I have discussed some of these in detail. The Richards paradox of the class of all numbers definable with less than one hundred words is a good example. The paradox is exhibited in the following way. There is a finite number of combinations of one hundred words and therefore a finite number of numbers definable with one hundred words. These numbers must contain a largest number. Now write the number larger by unity than the largest of these. This is a number defined with less than one hundred words, as may be verified by counting the words just written, and is therefore in the class. But it is by construction not a member of the class. The paradox arises because the terms have not sufficient fixity of meaning. A definite collection of words need not fix uniquely a number, but the number defined by the words may change with the context in which the words are embedded, and in particular may change with the passage of time.

It may be remarked in passing that this method of logical analysis, namely by analyzing the properties of the verbal specification of the process, has now largely fallen into disuse, although at one time it appeared promising and was exploited by various mathematicians. I believe that the reason it fell into disuse was not that the dangers incident to its use, such as we have just seen, were clearly recognized, but that it proved sterile in producing useful results. One suspects that it would not have proved sterile if it had rested on a sound basis.

# V. MATHEMATICS

WE ARE now ready to pass on from these matters of pure logic which we have just discussed to a consideration of some of the applications of logic in mathematics, which is usually recognized to be properly a branch of logic. We may well begin this consideration by recalling our discussion of the transcendence of $\pi$, for this brings out at once some of the connections between logic and mathematics. The thinking of most mathematicians is, I believe, very sympathetic to the view that $\pi$ is either transcendental or not, that it has this property in its own right, independent of what I think about it; that if I am clever I will discover some way of finding whether it has this property or not, but even if I am not clever enough I must still recognize that some process is "possible" by which it may be determined. This concept of "possible" bulks large in the mind of many mathematicians. In a recent article in *Philosophy of Science* there is this definition: "Mathematics is the language of the possible." This seems to present clearly a common point of view. The concept of "possible" is tied up closely with another almost indispensable concept of the mathematician, namely "existence," as one may see by a paraphrase of what possible means, namely a world would be a possible world if it *might exist*. What is the operational meaning of the words possible and exist; do they apply in all cases, or exactly and without approximation in any case?

The question of existence usually arises in connection with questions as to the possibility of certain properties or combinations of properties, and may take this form: Do objects exist with certain properties? We are to seek the operational meaning of existence in what we do in order to answer such a question. Consider a simple example: "Does an odd number exist with an even square"? If we do not know the answer to this question, I suppose that our first impulse would be to search around to see whether we could find an odd number with an even square. That is, our first impulse would be to try to exhibit a number with the desired properties. And if we succeeded in exhibiting such a number, our answer would be "yes." In making this answer, however, we would of course have to make the preliminary assumption that numbers themselves exist. What we mean by this it seems to me is at the bottom of the whole matter, and we will return to it. For the present, we note merely that exhibition of something already known to exist, which can be shown to have the properties in question, constitutes a positive answer to the question. But in this special case we convince ourselves after a little trial that we shall not be successful in exhibiting such a number, and we are driven to try another line of attack. We assume that some one has exhibited such a number to us, and we then engage to show a contradiction. This we know we can do in this case, and we therefore conclude that such a number does not exist. In coming to this conclusion we tacitly assume that self-contradiction and existence are mutually exclusive, that is, that nothing exists which is self-contradictory.

Consider another sort of example, in which we are not able to exhibit a specific example which has the properties in question, nor are able to prove that the possession of such properties would involve a contradiction. There are cases of this kind in which we are able to show that the assumption of the "opposite" properties would lead to contradiction. If we can do this, then we also say that the object exists.

This kind of "existence" is, however, obviously a different sort of thing operationally than the existence that can be exhibited. Why is it that we use the same word for it? I suppose that the reason is that if we can establish this second sort of existence we proceed to do the same sort of thing with it that we do with the first. That is, we proceed on the assumption that if we act as if the object did exist we shall never encounter a contradiction. Why is it that we feel safe in this assumption? To answer this question we have to go back and inquire what we meant by "opposite" properties. What we want to mean is something all-inclusive, so that the object must either have certain properties, or their opposite, and there is no other possibility. In order to secure this, the specification of the "opposite" is usually put in the form of a negative: the opposite of the property $A$ is not-$A$. It is in most cases of mathematical interest doubtless possible to make this clean-cut division, as we can say that an integer is either odd or it is not odd. But when we come to deal with physical objects we have seen that it is usually not possible, as for instance, we cannot say: a color is either green or it is not green. It seems to me that we would not grant the status of existence to an object on the strength of a proof that the opposite led to contradiction unless we were convinced that the division into $A$ and not-$A$ was all-inclusive. If there is a third possibility, what is the point in showing that not-$A$ is contradictory; there seems to be no necessity in such a case that $A$ be free from contradiction, which is obviously what is wanted. It would appear, therefore, that one must be careful in using this method of proof of existence. In particular, with regard to certain mathematical concepts we have seen that all-inclusiveness fails when application is made to infinite aggregates, as for example, we cannot say that a statement is either true or it is not true.

Is there not another possibility in addition to those which we have considered? Suppose we can neither exhibit an example, nor prove that the assumption of exhibition leads to contradiction, nor prove that the assumption of the contrary leads to contradiction, could we not conceivably prove that the assumption of existence could not lead to contradiction?

If we could, I think we would be willing to assume existence. As a matter of fact, however, it appears that this sort of a proof has never been given, and there is recent very important analysis in logic which seems to show that such a proof is not possible without going out of the original universe of discourse. Let us suppose, however, that by some method or other, short of rigorous proof, and by going out of the system if necessary, we have made very plausible to ourselves that the assumption of an entity with certain properties would not lead to contradiction. What would we then do about it? I think we would go right ahead as if it did exist, we would invent a new symbol for it, and use this symbol just like the symbol for things which we knew did exist, and presently the next generation would forget about the origin of the symbol, and suppose that the thing existed like any other thing. That is, we have here invented or created a concept, and after the invention of it, it acts just as if it had existence.

This brings us back to the fundamental question. Suppose someone asks me how I am sure that the thing I exhibit exists: For example, suppose I exhibit a circle as an answer to the question: does a figure exist which has infinitely valued rotational symmetry? How do I know that a circle exists? A circle is defined as the plane figure all of whose points are equally distant from the same point. The circle is defined in terms of its properties, and it has not been proved, and indeed it cannot be proved in the system of geometry itself, that in the assumption of these properties there may not lie concealed a contradiction, which some mathematician may be clever enough to unearth at some future time.

A similar question occurs if the thing is defined in terms of operations; namely, how do I know that the operations can be performed which I assumed in the definition? In particular, the system of natural numbers is generated by successively adding unity; how do I know that I can add one to any number, or how do I know that the numbers exist? Or to ask a still more fundamental question: how do I know that the tables, the clouds, and the stars of ordinary experience exist? These are not given directly in experience, but are constructions. It seems to me that the answer to all these questions is that the things exist because for one thing the concepts work in the way that I want them to. In my effort to solve the problem of adapting myself to my environment I invent certain devices, and some of these are successful and I use them in my thinking. Existence is a term which presupposes the success of certain of these devices. The concept of table and cloud and star is successful in dealing with certain aspects of my experience; hence they "exist." In short, this is the operational meaning of existence. The concept of number is similarly successful in dealing with certain aspects of experience, as in finding whether my children have all come in to dinner or whether my neighbor is giving me as many apples as he should for my turnips; if they had not attained this success, numbers would not "exist." The fundamental requirement in a mathematical object like a number is that the use of it should not lead to contradiction.

To the question of how we know that a particular concept is successful—for example how we know that the concept of numbers can never lead to contradiction—the only possible answer is the answer of experience: the concepts are successful because we have tried them and they work. We use a concept in all possible situations and if we never run into trouble with it, we begin to feel safe with it, and grant it the status of "existence." In particular, numbers have been an astonishingly successful device, and it is difficult to visualize situations in which they might lead to contradiction; but no proof can be given, and it may be that situations of this sort are now arising in physics, for we know that electrons cannot be thought of as having identity, and therefore as being countable in the ordinary way. Indeed we are already pretty well convinced that the concepts of space and time have proved unsuccessful when carried inside the atom; and why may not the concept of number?

Mathematics thus appears to be ultimately just as truly an empirical science as physics or chemistry, and the feeling that it is something essentially different arises only when we do not carry our analysis far enough. A true appreciation of the empirical character of mathematics I believe to be particularly important for the physicist now that mathematics is coming to play such a glorified rôle in physics.

If mathematics is ultimately an experimental science, what shall we say to the description of mathematics as the language of the possible? The implication clearly is that mathematics is not limited simply to results that have been proved or to situations that have been investigated, but goes further and says something about anything that we might do at any time in the future. The reason that this sort of a description has appeal must be sought in the realization of mathematicians that the objects and concepts of mathematics are not subject to the same sort of control as the objects of our material experience. It is obvious that "possible" is not used with all the connotations of its use in daily life, for it makes sense to say in daily life, "It is *possible* that the future may break entirely with the past," whereas this is just the one sort of thing that the mathematician does not mean by possible. Such a concept of possible in mathematics would obviously lead only to chaos. The primary control of the concepts of mathematics is that contradiction should not be involved, whereas a concept like that of the "table" is subject to other controls, such, for example, as that it have identity, and that it have continued existence in time. It is meaningless to ask whether the number 10 which I am thinking of now is really the same as the number 10 which you are thinking of, or whether it continues to have a real existence whether I think of it or not. Because objects of mathematics are subjected to less restrictive controls, they are capable of a much greater wealth of combination than the objects of daily experience. A result of this is that combinations satisfying *only* the principle of contradiction *need* not be expected to have their counterpart in actual experience.

If we define as "possible" all those concepts which do not involve a contradiction, which seems to be the meaning of possible as it is used, then mathematics must be admitted to be, almost by definition, the language of the possible. But if we go further and imply that we have here some monstrous method of penetrating into the future, or that mathematics can give us something not involved somehow in past experience or that it is more than an epitome of certain aspects of past experience in compact form, then I believe that we are assuming a palpably false position, which disregards the experimental character of mathematics.

We are now in a position to ask whether the category of existence is all-inclusive. Can I, for example, say, "Somewhere in the decimal expansion of $\pi$ there either exists the sequence 0123456789 or it does not exist"? The answer to this question must be the same as our answer with regard to truth; the operations involved in the concept of existence are obviously not broad enough to be exhaustive in this case, for we can neither exhibit the sequence, nor show that if we had such a sequence we would have contradiction, nor show that if we had such a sequence we would not have contradiction, nor show that if we could not exhibit such a sequence we would or would not have contradiction. It follows that in general the concept is not all-inclusive—the law of the excluded middle does not apply, and I cannot say a thing either exists or it does not exist.

Does the criterion of existence which has evolved out of this discussion, namely either exhibition of an example, or proof that the assumption of non-existence would lead to a contradiction, cover everything that the mathematician has in the back of his head in his concept of existence? I believe that it does not, as we can see from the following example. I suppose that anyone will agree that ten digits written down in sequence and interpreted according to the Arabic convention represents a number. Let us now define a certain number as the sequence of ten digits that will be obtained when a certain roulette wheel is spun the next ten times. The question is whether the number defined in this way exists or not? I believe that most mathematicians would claim that the number defined in this way does not exist. But this number can clearly be exhibited—all I have to do is to spin the roulette wheel and there it is, all exhibited!

Or if the use of a piece of mechanism in defining the number appears illegitimate, because the mechanism is not defined in mathematical terms, and perhaps might not even spin when we wanted it to, we define the number as the sequence of ten digits which I write down at random when first asked to exhibit it. There can now be no such objection, because we must assume that I will not fail to write down the digits when required, since mathematics is itself an exercise of the human intellect, and requires as a presupposition that the human intellect is a going concern. In fact, we have about the strongest possible case here, for I know I can exhibit the number, I am convinced that the assumption that I can exhibit it does not lead to contradiction (proved perhaps by going out of the system) and I know that the assumption that I could not exhibit it would lead to contradiction, because this would lead to the conclusion that I could not do mathematics.

Yet I think that nevertheless most mathematicians do not grant the status of existence to the number defined in this

way. The reason, I think, is that they cannot think of this
number in the same way that they think of the material things
of everyday experience, which afford the examples of existence par excellence. This number cannot be thought of as
"there" in the same sense as a thing can be thought of as
"there." The reason of course is that the operation which
determines the number has not yet been carried out, and to
assume that it has been carried out leads us into a situation
that has to be ruled out. It does not land us in *contradiction*
to assume that the operation has been carried out, for obviously all possible combinations of ten digits might already
have been obtained by spinning roulette wheels enough
times, but it does land us in contradiction with the fundamental properties of roulette wheels to assume that we could
now know what the number is that had been so produced.
But even if the assumption that the operation has been carried
out does not land us in contradiction, it does bring us into
conflict with the fundamental limitation that operations have
to be performed in time, and that the future is in principle
unknowable. Things defined therefore in terms of intrinsically future operations (specifying a roulette wheel was
merely a way of assuring that the operation was *intrinsically*
in the future) are not granted the status of existence by mathematicians. The reason why the mathematician refuses to concern himself with things of this sort is obviously that they are
without interest to him because their properties are not defined with sufficient precision; if the properties could be
known with complete precision, the number could be exhibited now, and hence would now be "in existence."

It seems then that mathematical objects do not exist for
the mathematician unless it can be assumed without contradiction, or other violation of fundamental requirements, that
the operations by which they are exhibited have already been
performed. The fact that there may be other requirements

than merely freedom from contradiction, seems to be seldom explicitly stated, although it may be implicitly assumed, as in the example above.

A mathematician often talks of another kind of existence than the existence of mathematical objects, namely the existence of mathematical relations. What does it mean to ask whether a relation exists, such for example: "Is there a relation between the square of a number and the square of its double?" The answer is evidently yes in this case, because I can exhibit the relation, namely the square of a number is always one-fourth of the square of its double. Exhibition of a relation obviously implies a proof, which is self-evident in this case. What about relations that cannot be exhibited, as when the proof cannot be given? For example, is there a relation between an integer and the number of primes less than it, or can I write down an expression for the $n$th prime number? It is to be remarked in the first place that these problems are not quite definitely formulated; there is a sense in which the answer must be definitely yes, because if I am given any definite number $n$ I can always find by a finite number of steps how many primes there are less than it, or I can find the first $n$ primes. But this is obviously not what is intended. What I wanted was some simple closed expression, such as a polynomial. But what sorts of function can be used in writing out this expression, and what does closed mean? May I use factorials, or gamma functions, or elliptic integrals, or what is the limit? If there is no limit, why do I not invent a new function, the number of primes less than $n$, and endow it with a new symbol, and use this? I am convinced that such can never lead to contradiction. The problem therefore obviously has to be artificially limited.

Suppose, then, that I agree to allow only particular sorts of function, so that the problem is well defined, and these functions are ones whose properties are already fully understood, and whose relations have been worked out, so that there is no danger of the problem reducing to a triviality, then is it the feeling of the mathematician that a solution exists or not? Of course if he can show that the assumption that a solution exists leads to a contradiction he will say that it does not exist. But suppose that this cannot be done, as for example the proof of the statement, "To assume that $e^e$ is the root of an algebraic equation leads to a contradiction," has not been given. Or what happens when I have exhibited a relation which purports to be the relation but no proof has been given. There are a number of cases of this sort in number theory, for example, in which suspected relations have not been established. In such cases the problem reduces to answering the question: Is a certain relation true or not true? The preceding discussion of truth is pertinent, and we conclude that the concept of truth is not applicable in such cases.

Nevertheless I believe as a matter of observation that most mathematicians believe with respect to such relations as these, namely relations which are couched in reasonable appearing language, that it will some day be found possible either to exhibit an example, or else to prove that the contrary involves a contradiction. It is because they have this belief that they want to say: "The relation either does or does not exist, and if it does exist it may some day be discovered." It seems to me that as long as there is no ultimate criterion of freedom from contradiction except experimentation, this point of view is certainly not justified, and we must recognize that the concept of existence is not inclusive enough to cover all questions that we can ask about relations as well as about objects, and we must simply say that until proof to the contrary is given, the concept does not apply. The operational point of view would say that the relation comes into existence when it is discovered. It is curious that apparently the mathematician never speaks of creating, yet why is it not a useful and suggestive description, to say, for example, that the first irrational, the square root of 2, was created, or invented if preferred, when the procedure was devised for setting it up? The feeling of mathematicians that relations either exist or not, whether or no, doubtless has its explanation in its success, for a great many suspected relations have been found after diligent search, and the conviction of the possibility of success has doubtless been an important psychological factor in bringing about success. But this seems to me to be merely one of those attitudes that it is always possible to maintain, for if I am successful and find the relation, that is that, and all there is to it, whereas if I do not find it or show that it leads to contradiction, I can always say that I may do it tomorrow. The mere fact that it is always possible to maintain this attitude suggests that it can have no very deep significance.

We may summarize this discussion of the fundamental characteristics and limitations of mathematics as follows: mathematics is ultimately an experimental science, for freedom from contradiction cannot be proved, but only postulated and checked by observation, and similarly existence can only be postulated and checked by observation. Furthermore, mathematics requires the fundamental device of practically all thought, of analyzing experience into static bits with static meanings. In this respect mathematics fails to reproduce with complete fidelity the obvious fact that experience is not composed of static bits, but is a string of activity, or the fact that the use of language is an activity, and the total meanings of terms are determined by the matrix in which they are embedded. The mathematical concept of time appears to be particularly remote from the time of experience. We may, therefore, not anticipate complete success by mathematics in meeting all actual situations.

# VI. MATHEMATICS IN APPLICATION

AFTER all this analysis of the fundamental nature of mathematics, which of course disregards many important questions, but which is I believe sufficient for our purposes, let us inquire what we do in applying mathematics to any concrete physical problem, or in attempting to set up a mathematical theory of some physical phenomenon.

In particular, let us suppose that I am presented with a set of equations by the theoretical physicist, which he tells me contains the theory of the phenomenon in question. In checking this statement, that is in attempting to apply the equations, I discover at once that the equations are only part of the story. The equations always have to be accompanied by a "text" telling what the significance of the equations is and how to use them. Thus if I set up the mathematical theory of a body falling under the action of gravity, I have the equation $dv/dt = g,$ but I have to supplement this by a "text," saying that $v$ is a number describing a property of the moving body which can be obtained by a certain kind of measurement, which is specified, that $t$ is the time obtained by another kind of measurement, etc. The equation then determines by integration or other mathematical operation a system of numbers. For example the equation above gives by integration $v = gt + v_0$ or $s = \dfrac{gt^2}{2} + v_0\, t + s_0.$ What I mean by saying that the equations contain a theory of the falling body is that numbers obtainable by the physical manipulations stipulated in the text satisfy the equation when substituted into it. Not only must the text describe the nature of the measurement, but it must also specify the connection between the different symbols in the equation. Thus in our simple example the text specifies that the $s$ and the $t$ are the distance and time obtained by *simultaneous* measurements. The equation itself has no mechanism for demanding that $s$ and $t$ be simultaneous, and in fact this demand cannot be described in the language of the equation.

Suppose that the free fall of the body is terminated by a lake. The equation must be replaced by something like $dv/dt = -av^2$, perhaps, and the text must in addition to its other duties, inform us when to replace the one equation by the other. Or the text may be used in other ways; it may enable us to select from the results of a mathematical manipulation that one which has the proper significance. For example, in the simple mathematical theory of such financial transactions as get into elementary text-books of algebra, the text, which is usually suppressed, instructs us to discard the negative and imaginary roots of equations.

It appears, therefore, that a complete mathematical formulation requires equations plus text, and the text may perform a variety of functions. The necessity for a text is almost always overlooked, but I think it must be recognized to be essential, and a study of what it must contain is as necessary for an adequate conception of the nature of the mathematical theory as is a study of the equations themselves.

One of the functions of the text, we have seen, is to tell us how to set up the correspondence between the numbers given by the equation and the numbers obtained by manipulations of the physical system. The text cannot tell us what it is that the correspondence is to be set up with without going outside the system of the mathematical theory and assuming an intuitive knowledge of the language of ordinary experience. In classical mechanics, the geometrical variables in the equations of motion are the coordinates of massive particles, but unless we know intuitively what a massive particle is, we simply cannot make connection with equation or theory. Not only is the theory powerless to describe, either in text or equations, what the elements are to which correspondences are to be made, but all the more is it powerless to explain why the elements have the properties that they do. Mass can have no explanation in mechanics. Classical electrodynamics was felt to be a great advance because it gave an explanation of mass. But mass was explained at the expense of making the electron the ultimate, and classical electrodynamics can give no answer to such questions as: what is electricity, why does electricity come in discrete units or why does it repel itself?

In general, it appears then that a mathematical theory enables us to set up correspondences between the mathematical quantities of the equations and the measured quantities of experience. A clear recognition of this has led to a rather altered idea of the way in which our mathematical theories may be usefully constructed. Formerly mathematical theories usually had in the background a physical model of some sort, as, for example, the kinetic theory of gases had in the background a model consisting of idealized molecules, and this in spite of the fact that the phenomena of spectrum analysis, for example, were evidence enough that actual molecules could not be as simple as this. The molecules were so simplified that they were amenable to mathematical treatment. We had then a sort of double theory—a mathematical theory of the idealized model, and then a physical theory consisting of the statement that there was a correspondence between the idealized model and the actual physical system sufficiently close so that certain properties of the physical system were reproduced by the model. The point in making such an idealized physical model was that it had a mathematical theory simple enough to be handled.

It presently appeared to reflection, however, that there was an unnecessary step here—since all that could be done in any event was to set up certain correspondences between the results of the mathematical manipulations and the physical system, why have the intermediate step of the idealized physical model, since a correspondence to a correspondence is also a correspondence? This of course is exactly what has been done in recent wave mechanical theories, particularly that of Dirac, and we know that such a procedure has been brilliantly successful. I think that the reason that this change of attitude was so long deferred was that it was not realized that there was an intermediate step—the idealized physical model was felt to be so much like the actual physical system, or at any rate the endeavor was to make it so much like the physical system, that the model was actually identified with the physical system.

What we now have is in effect mathematical models rather than physical models. This emancipation I feel to be a very important step forward toward greater theoretical power, because there is an enormously greater wealth of possibility among the structures of mathematics than in the physical models which we can visualize and which have a simple enough mathematical theory. It cannot be denied, however, that a mathematical model cannot be visualized in the same sense that a physical model can be. Although we may recognize with our intellect that the mathematical model is just as good as the physical model if it only enables us to answer any question that we may propose about the behavior of the physical system, nevertheless we have an uncomfortable feeling that we have lost something.

I think that we discover on analysis that it is the explanation which we feel we have lost. This of course brings up the whole question of the nature of an explanation; since I have attempted to analyze this in my *Logic of Modern Physics* a brief statement must suffice here. One finds, I think, that complete explanation is never possible, but that ultimately we come out with something that cannot be explained, and which has to be merely accepted as a commonplace of experience. Explanation consists merely in analyzing our complicated systems into simpler systems in such a way that we recognize in the complicated system the interplay of elements already so familiar to us that we accept them as not needing explanation. A theory which uses a physical model is therefore at the same time an "explanation" if one can find in the actual physical system the counterpart of the assumed elements of the physical model. The kinetic theory of gases did, accordingly, constitute an explanation of the behavior of a gas in a sense which the purely mathematical model, consisting of the first and second laws of thermodynamics and a characteristic function or two, could not, because there is evidence from other phenomena of the existence in the gas of molecules as postulated in the physical model. It is true that the physical model granted only mass and moment of inertia to the molecules, ignoring any other possible properties, but this in effect was part of the theory, and it was assumed that any other properties were not important because the effect of them would average out from the behavior of a large assemblage. There is a further point: when the elements of the physical model have recognizable counterparts in the physical system, the question of why the correspondence between the model and the physical system is to be set up in the particular way that it is does not present itself, the method of correspondence by identification being so simple as to call for no discussion. In the case of the mathematical model on the other hand, any sort of arbitrary correspondence will serve, provided only that it is definite enough. It would appear therefore that the mathematical model gives up the possibility of explanation in the usual sense.

I think that the ordinary physicist will want to keep his physical models as long as he can. But suppose the new physical experience of which we are trying to form a theory is so far removed from ordinary experience that we cannot find in it the counterpart of any of the objects of ordinary experience. Under such conditions it would seem that an explanation in the ordinary sense is impossible, and recourse to a mathematical model of some sort becomes just as satisfactory as recourse to a physical model.

This of course is what has happened in wave mechanics. Apparently we have got down to a realm of phenomena where some of the most fundamental modes of thought— space, time, and identifiability—are no longer applicable, and whether or not Dirac's theory is inevitable, it must be recognized that in using a purely mathematical model it is performing a most useful service in emphasizing this aspect of the situation. Whether we are willing to say that a mathematical model like this affords an "explanation" is to a large extent a matter of taste and of words. Or whether we would accept the contention of the purists that it is evidence of weakmindedness to yearn for any other sort of explanation is also perhaps a personal matter. But unless one has supreme power as a mathematician, one may well find it useful to have at his command methods of reasoning by analogy that will give him an insight into the nature of the solution of special problems, and one may cheer from the sidelines any attempt to invent combinations of the elements of the mathematical analysis which may be handled somewhat like the elements of ordinary experience, and of which we may hope ultimately to acquire a more intuitive command. I suspect that Bohr's attempt to find a dualistic aspect of nature is an attempt of this sort.

Another interesting aspect of mathematical models has been emphasized by Heisenberg. At the beginning of the century it was often emphasized in studying mathematical physics that every step in the mathematical manipulation of the equations had its counterpart in some feature of the physical system, and that one did not have a real grasp of the mathematical theory until one could see in detail the working out of this parallelism. Heisenberg's point of view appears rather like a glorified combination of this point of view and the dictum of the operationist that only those physical concepts have meaning which can be defined in terms of physical operations, which means in particular that no quantitative physical concept has meaning unless it corresponds to something measurable. Since every equation of physics essentially deals with numbers, Heisenberg demanded that only those quantities shall enter the equations which are intrinsically measurable. Bohr's atom was an example of the other sort of thing, for there was no physical evidence for the existence of the discrete orbits, but only of the frequencies emitted when the electron made the "jump" (for which again there was no physical evidence) from one orbit to another. The frequencies are of course measurable, and Heisenberg's matrix form of wave mechanics did as a matter of fact use only these frequencies, without introducing the superfluous notion of orbits. I have always wondered, however, whether perhaps this requirement of Heisenberg was not formulated after the event as a sort of philosophical justification for its success, rather than having played an indispensable part in the formulation of the theory. For in spite of its rational ring, and the fact that it appears to meet the demands of operationism, there seems to be no necessity for it from the point of view about mathematical models which we have just been discussing. All that is required of the theory is that it should provide the tools for calculating the behavior of the physical system, and it is capable of doing this if there is correspondence between those aspects of the physical system which it engages to reproduce and *some* of the results of the mathematical manipulations. For instance, the closing price of a stock on the six business days of the week may be adequately represented by a polynomial of the sixth degree. In using this polynomial to get the desired information there has to be a text stating that the answer can be obtained by substituting into the polynomial the proper *integer*. It is impossible to construct this formula so that the mathematical operation of substituting fractional numbers may not also be carried out. Such manipulation with fractional numbers obviously need have no physical significance, although a broker to whom this formula was presented out of whole cloth would certainly be tempted to find the state of the market at 12 M. of each day by substituting fractional numbers. The broker might even flatter himself that he was making some progress until he made the staggering observation that the stock market is open only from 10 to 3.

There would seem to be no necessity therefore, inherent in the requirements of the model itself, that all mathematical operations should correspond to recognizable processes in the physical system. Nor is there any more any reason why all the *symbols* appearing in the fundamental mathematical equations should have their physical counterpart, nor why purely auxiliary mathematical quantities should not be invented to facilitate the mathematical manipulations, if that proves possible. In fact this sort of thing was done long ago in classical mathematical physics. A good example is the stress inside a solid body of the theory of elasticity. A stress is never measured as such, but is a purely constructional quantity, an aggregate of six components, which can be calculated from the elastic constants, the surface forces and other suitable combinations of data, and which is serviceable because from it the forces acting across the free face of the solid, which are directly measurable, can in turn be easily calculated. Whether or not physical "reality" should be ascribed to the stress, as many people do, is largely an academic matter; the important point is that we have here found it very convenient to introduce a quantity which is certainly not directly measured. I can see no objection to this sort of thing, nor can I understand why Heisenberg's principle has been so much talked about; as a guiding principle it appears to have been sterile or even positively misleading, and it is certainly given up in Dirac's form of wave mechanics.

The feeling that all the steps in a mathematical theory must have their counterpart in the physical system is the outgrowth, I think, of a certain mystical feeling about the mathematical construction of the physical world. Some sort of an idea like this has been flitting about in the background of the paraphernalia of the thinking of civilization at least since the days of Pythagoras, and every now and then, perhaps after some particularly striking mathematical success, it bursts forth again like a crop of mushrooms after a rain, as in the recent fervid exclamation of Jeans that "God is a mathematician." This mystical feeling involves, I think, a feeling for the "real existence" of principles according to which this universe is run. We have seen how meaningless is the contention that principles exist independent of the mind in which they are formulated. What Jeans might have said is that Man is a mathematician, and reflected that it is no accident that he forms nature in his own image.

The search for a general eternal underlying principle is, I think, a result of the striving of the mind for "explanation." This striving must be resisted when carried beyond a certain point, and the fact that we must resist it is merely another bit of evidence that we have not yet got our thinking under such complete control that it is applicable to all aspects of experience. Our difficulty in resisting this primeval urge of our mind for explanation is somewhat lessened by the recognition that mathematics is an experimental science, explicitly developed to deal with the quantitative aspects of experience, and it would certainly be surprising if mathematics did not continue to be applicable in some form or other as long as experience continues to present quantitative aspects.

There is one respect in addition to those already discussed, and which I feel to be very important, in which the structure of mathematics is obviously entirely different from that of experience, namely in that the equations of mathematics contain nothing to restrict their range of application. For example, the equation of a falling body, is indifferent to whether we substitute into it a time of $10^{-100}$ or $10^{+100}$ seconds, both of them numbers with absolutely no physical significance whatever; the equation will, however, cheerfully supply us with a corresponding distance, ignoring the futility of its result. In this particular example no harm ever results because we instinctively know how to limit the applicability of the formula, but there are other situations in physics where the results have been more serious. Perhaps the most striking example is in the electron theory of Lorentz, which consisted in an extension to the atomic and electronic level of the field equations of Maxwell. These equations had their direct experimental check in large-scale phenomena; the extension of the equations to small-scale phenomena was a hypothetical step, to be justified by its success. The fields which enter the equations must fluctuate widely in the neighborhood of electrons and are not capable of direct measurement, so that we are here dealing with a construction, just as we have seen a mechanical stress is a construction. The equations for the field of force about an electron were obviously not capable of holding indefinitely close to the center of the electron, because there were difficulties with convergence. It was therefore assumed that the electron had a finite radius, but the hypothesis was made that the equations still continue to hold inside the electron, the parts of the electron exerting forces on each other as if they were large-scale things, and from this hypothesis a value was computed for the radius of the electron. In recognizing that the electron has parts which repel each other we picture it as an ordinary mechanical thing; we then are led to ask what it is that holds the electron together. To this question the field equations have no answer, but we have to say arbitrarily that there are non-electrical forces which do not come within our scheme. The necessity for asserting non-electrical forces is felt to be a reproach. All these difficulties we were led into by pushing the range of application of the equations to the mathematical limit, without attending to the limitations of the corresponding physical measurements.

It seems to me that situations of this kind can at present only be dealt with through the text that must accompany the equations. The text should carry a statement that the equations cease to be valid when too close to the center of the electron, and state what to do then. We might conceivably, if it appears useful, replace the original equations by others inside the electron, the precise kind to be determined by trial. It would then have to be recognized that most of the content of such equations must be purely mathematical, introduced for convenience, because the detailed statements of the equations can be subject to no possible immediate experimental control. Or, and it seems to me preferable, the text might contain a statement simply to the effect that the electron must be treated as a whole, and that it reacts in a certain definite way in the presence of certain types of field at a limiting distance. If technical difficulties arise because the external field is not properly determined unless it is given at every point of the sphere which limits its range, then the text must formulate hypotheses about the connection between the gross behavior of the electron and the detailed distribution of the external field on the limiting sphere.

There seems, however, to be a curious reluctance to use the text in any such way. It is often stated that such a restriction of the range of application of an equation by a text is "artificial," with apparently the implication that it must also be incorrect. The demand seems to be for a single closed analytical expression which shall hold right up to the center of the electron, as in the recent field theory of Born and Infeld.[1] It seems to me that there is nothing "artificial" in the use of the text in the way suggested, for we have seen that there must always be a text somewhere in the background, and in fact, until some mathematical device is invented by which the equations automatically limit their own range of applicability, such a use of the text is necessary and just as integral a part of the mathematical theory as the equations themselves. It would perhaps be legitimate to object to a text which instructed us to stay outside the electron on the ground that we had thereby given up all hope of giving a theory of the electron itself, but I think that not even Lorentz himself would have maintained that his theory was a theory of the electron, but would have accepted the electron as given.

What is the basis for the feeling that a theory should not employ two different sorts of mathematical function, joined by a text instructing us when to switch from one to the other? Objection might of course be made on the ground of elegance, and doubtless in some cases on the ground of convenience in calculation, but I think that there is often a little feeling in the background that a mathematical formulation "really exists" and that the chances of our having found it are considerably less good as long as the tool marks of our handiwork are as evident as they are with two different analytical expressions. But I think this view overlooks

[1] M. Born and L. Infeld, "Foundations of the New Field Theory," *Proc. Roy. Soc.*, 144, 425, 1934.

the human and experimental nature of mathematics; there is no reason why the complete structure of two mathematical equations plus text is not just as truly mathematics as one equation plus text, for text of some sort there must always be. The use of two analytical expressions is merely a special case of the method of successive approximations which we have seen we have to use in all our thinking, and it would seem to be a Utopian ideal to hope that we could ever get rid of it completely in mathematics.

# VII. RELATIVITY

W E HAVE seen that for a complete appraisal of what is contained in any mathematical theory an analysis of the text is just as essential as an analysis of the equations. In particular, the text contains the unanalyzables of the theory and thus involves its essential limitations. Let us now examine the general theory of relativity from the point of view of the text. The text is never explicitly stated in formulations of the theory, so that we shall have to construct it for ourselves by observing how the equations are used. Consider any of the fundamental equations of relativity theory, as for example the equation of light propagation $ds^2 = 0 = \Sigma g_{mn} dx_m dx_n$, or the equation of motion of a particle $\frac{d^2 x_\mu}{ds^2} + \left\lceil \begin{matrix} \mu \\ \alpha\beta \end{matrix} \right. \frac{dx_\alpha}{ds} \frac{dx_\beta}{ds} = 0$, or one of the field equations. What is the operational meaning of the various symbols?

We have in the first place space and time coordinates, and in the second place physical happenings of various sorts to which these coordinates apply. In order to determine the coordinates of any happening, a framework of some kind must be constructed. This must be a *physical* framework, consisting perhaps of a grid of measuring rods with clocks at their points of intersection, for unless some sort of physical substratum is imagined for the framework we have not even the possibility of identifying the points of the framework. The necessary physical properties of this framework are not usually analyzed in any detail; we are usually satisfied with the statement that it is of no consequence of what the measuring rods are constructed so long as they are rigid, without any very articulate analysis of what is meant by "rigid." The specification of what is meant by a clock is usually even less articulate, and has been felt to be a matter of much difficulty by a number of critics. The deduction of the shift toward the red of light emitted in a gravitational field reduces to the question of whether the radiating atom is a clock or not, and the answer to this question has been made only on the basis of various arguments from plausibility, which are more or less intuitive in character and without precision. In fact, in practice it almost appears as though the only criterion for a clock is whether it functions in the way that the equations demand that a clock function. The framework therefore appears to offer difficulties which I believe have not been adequately resolved.

Passing over these difficulties, what sort of physical happening is it whose coordinates are determined by the framework? The equations themselves have no means of specifying what this is, but this is the task of the text. Inspection of the equations shows that the sort of happening is different in the different equations. Thus in the equation of light propagation, the happening whose coordinates satisfy the equation is the arrival of a light signal. The equation has to presuppose that we know what we mean by the arrival of a light signal. Furthermore, the equation involves the arrival of the light signal at different points of the framework, so that in addition we must know what we mean by the arrival of the *same* light signal at different points before the equation can have operational meaning. The method of apprehension of the light signal is not analyzed, and is one of the ultimates of the theory. If the equation is the equation of motion of a particle, then the happening whose coordinates appear in the equation is the arrival of a material particle at various points of the framework. What we mean by a particle is not analyzed, but is accepted as an ultimate; the particle must have certain properties: in particular, it can be identified, and its motion followed from point to point so that we can say that now the *same* particle is arriving at this point which a moment ago arrived at that point—otherwise the equation has no meaning. If the equation is one of the field equations, involving a gravitational potential, then the happening whose coordinates appear in the equation is a complex thing, involving measurements according to definite procedures. In all cases, whatever the nature of the happening, we have to be able to correlate the happening with a point of the framework. The establishment of this coincidence is supposed to be intuitively possible, and is one of the unanalyzables of the theory.

The equations may thus involve various sorts of physical operation and may deal with more than one kind of unanalyzable, all of which must be specified in the text, but in all cases *happening* of some sort there must be at a point of the framework if the equations are to have real content. This fact, that we can only talk about happenings of one sort or another in a framework is often lost sight of and there is a strong tendency to concentrate attention on the coordinates themselves, disregarding the quality of the happening. In fact, the aggregate of four coordinates, three of space and one of time, has been given a technical name, the "event." This it seems to me has unfortunate implications. Ordinary experience we think of as composed of events; these are obviously not events in the technical sense, but are rather what we have been calling "happenings." It seems to me that it must have been a confusion arising from this use of "event" which is responsible for the statement so often made that there is nothing in nature except pointer readings, or that "Alles ist Coincidenz." According to this point of view the universe is analyzed into world lines and the points of intersection of the world lines are stated to be the only things with physical significance. The fact that only the intersections of world lines can have physical significance is often made the basis for the argument that the equations must be covariant in form, for obviously the intersections remain no matter how the coordinate mesh is distorted. This has always seemed to me a most surprising point of view; it seems to overlook the fact that a world line by itself has no physical significance, but we must also know what it is the world line of. Let anyone who maintains that there is nothing in nature except pointer readings or coincidences, engage to reproduce the situation that gave rise to the pointer readings in terms only of the framework and the pointer readings themselves.

Since the equations of relativity accept different sorts of happening as unanalyzables, it follows that any complete description of a concrete physical phenomenon in terms of the equations of its world lines must be a rather complicated thing from the point of view of the text. For this must specify that one equation describes the world line of a particular kind of happening, such perhaps as the appearance of a particular sort of light signal at points of the framework, and another equation perhaps the appearance of a particle of definite mass, or another equation the appearance of an electron. Relativity theory apparently does not regard it as its task to attempt to analyze how many kinds of these unanalyzable intuitively recognizable elementary happenings would be necessary in order to characterize a definite physical situation exhaustively, in the sense that, given the equations and the framework and the text, the physical situation could be reproduced. Because it does not make this analysis and is content to operate with a number of unanalyzed happenings, it has apparently renounced the ambition to be a complete theory, in the sense that certain of the theories of the past have aspired to completeness. I suppose that one hundred and fifty years ago the mechanical school of physicists would have thought it probable that the course of any phenomenon could be reproduced in terms of an exhaustive characterization of the motion of elementary mass particles, and certainly in the early days of electron theory the belief was not uncommon that a physical situation would be reproduced if the motion of all the elementary electrical charges was reproduced.

Although relativity theory makes no very articulate attempt to specify the nature of its unanalyzable happenings, nevertheless very definite assumptions have to be made about the properties of these happenings, as may be seen from the way they are handled by the theory. A very important part of the mathematical machinery of the theory consists of transformation of coordinates from one framework to another. In this transformation of coordinates I think it is easy to confuse two things which are much alike, but nevertheless operationally quite recognizably different. It is in the first place to be remembered that what we are interested in is a transformation of the coordinates of *happenings*. We can deal unequivocally with a situation like the following. Given an observer (myself) and a series of definite physical happenings. Then I can find the coordinates of these happenings in one or another frame of reference. The process of correlating the coordinates of a definite happening in one frame with those in another is what constitutes the transformation of coordinates. This correlation can be unequivocally made because it is one of my unanalyzables to be able to apprehend the coincidence of the mesh points of one framework with those of another. Given now the coordinates in any of my many possible frames, the frame itself, and a specification of what elementary phenomenon it is that I have been observing, I will be able to reproduce uniquely the physical situation that gave rise to the observations. All this is straightforward enough; we have to demand only that the thing that is being reproduced is apprehended and has meaning from my individual point of view. It is obvious that with a set-up like this no physical conclusions whatever about the happening can be drawn merely by passing from the coordinates in one framework to those in another. But what is usually done is somewhat different. Two observers are imagined, each with his own frame of reference. Each observer determines in his framework the coordinates of a succession of physical happenings, and then the transformation of coordinates is accomplished by correlating the coordinates obtained by the two observers for what they agree are the *same* happenings. That is, the unanalyzables of the two observers have to possess, in addition to the intuitively apprehendable properties for each observer already implied, the further property that two different observers can unequivocally agree on a "sameness."

What does the assumption of this possibility involve? It is not as simple as it might appear, because the things to which "sameness" is being ascribed are unanalyzables, and the intuitive operations which define the unanalyzables are certainly not the "same," whatever that may mean, for the two observers. If one observer sees a flash of yellow light at a certain point of his framework, the other observer moving with high relative velocity may apprehend only a flash of infra red radiation by feeling a glow of heat on his finger. I think it would be difficult to persuade two observers to call an elementary event the same which was perceived by two totally different senses. It seems to me that the only basis for a secure judgment of "sameness" is a certain amount of discreteness in the elementary event. If happenings are discrete enough, one observer can say to the other "Something just happened to me," and the other can reply, "Something just happened to me too," and by definition we can call this the same event, provided no confusion arises from the overlapping of other events. But other events always do overlap to a certain extent, and it would probably be very difficult to give a rigorous definition of what would constitute prohibitive overlapping, or exactly what "enough" discreteness means.

There are other difficulties with the demand for discreteness. More often than not we have to deal with a series of events which are continuous from the large-scale point of view, as a massive particle moving along the measuring rod of one of the observers, whom we will call $A$. What are the discrete events by which the two observers $A$ and $B$ can describe this occurrence? From the standpoint of $A$ the situation is simple, because his measuring rod is ultimately atomic in structure and the discrete happenings are the arrival of the massive particle at the successive atoms of his rod. Similarly for $B$ the discrete events are the arrival of the particle at the atoms of his measuring rod. But these are not the events of which $A$ is aware. The only way by which $A$ and $B$ can give meaning to the "same" events is for $B$ to be able to watch the passage of the particle over the atoms of $A$'s scale, or vice versa. We now have identical events for $A$ and $B$. $B$ next has to give an approximate transcription to his own measuring rod; this will involve splitting atomic distances. That is, in order to be able to measure what happens in $A$'s system, $B$ has to use a more finely divided measuring rod than he used in the first place. This ultimately, for all possible particles, will demand an infinite fineness of subdivision of $B$'s rod, contrary to our original hypothesis that a measuring rod admits only a finite fineness of subdivision.

These considerations I believe may well raise doubts as to the fundamental assumption. We may be willing to assume that a given physical situation may be analyzed into discrete unresolvable elements by a single observer with sufficient lack of ambiguity for the purposes of certain physical theories, and at the same time question whether two different observers can analyze the same situation into discrete events in such a way that the two observers can attach a property of "sameness" to the events in addition to the other properties. Operationally it is evident that much more is involved in the second situation than in the first. It seems to me that the existence of this property of "sameness" acquires its plausibility in terms only of a feeling for an underlying "reality," which seems to me almost metaphysical in character, and to which I can see no way of giving sufficient operational sharpness.

There is another matter involved in the possibility of two observers agreeing on a property of sameness; they must be able to communicate with each other and unambiguously exchange meanings. This necessity for the exchange of meanings by two observers becomes even more insistent when we take the next step beyond a mere transformation of coordinates, and demand that the laws of nature be expressed in covariant form, independent of the coordinate system. Just what is meant by the "laws of nature" or by the laws being the same in different coordinate systems is somewhat vague, but apparently something like the following is contemplated. Similar observers are first imagined in the two frameworks. Just what "similar observers" means is also vague; the most vivid specification is to suppose that I myself first observe in one frame and then in the other. This of course involves the possibility of transferring myself from one frame to the other, something which obviously may present difficulties. However, given similar observers in the two frames, they are now supposed to make similar experiments in the two frames. Again what this means is vague; to make it specific we may suppose that each observer experiments according to directions written down in a book, and we may suppose that the same book is used by the two observers, which is transferred back and forth from one frame to the other as occasion arises. Whatever the precise details, it would seem that we must at least presuppose the possibility of the two observers communicating with each other, and that when communication has been established and meanings exchanged, the two observers find that they can pick out phenomena and operations in the two frames which they describe in the same language. In particular, the unanalyzable operations of the two observers must be described in the same language.

It seems to me that one may justifiably have serious misgivings at the apparent necessity of allowing such purely verbal notions to play a fundamental rôle in the theory. Surely there are unsettled questions with regard to language and meaning too puzzling for us to brush aside in the easy conviction that such considerations are of only academic importance. The feeling which many people apparently have that such considerations are only academic arises, I believe, from the narrow range of our experience. We know that we can talk successfully with a passing car, or that we can hold a wireless telephone conversation with a transcontinental train. But what happens when we have really high relative velocities, so that what one man sees another man hears, or what shall we say to the critic who asks us how we know that the printed words in the book or even the cerebrations of the observer may not experience a continuous shift of significance at high velocities or in an intense gravitational field? In any event it must strike one as paradoxical that in a theory of "relativity" it appears to be necessary to assume an absolute significance for language and meaning.

There is the further question as to what is meant by a "law of nature." Suppose that our observers were captious and refused to subscribe to what they might call our system of metaphysics, and claimed that they could find no so-called "law" in their experience, but all they could find was a succession of specific happenings, which they had found out how to describe and predict with any required degree of accuracy. One feels that one should not have to concern oneself with considerations of this character in order to put an ostensibly purely mathematical theory on a secure foundation. The extent to which the assumption of covariance is necessary in the fundamental argument of relativity theory seems to be something on which there is not clear-cut agreement, even by those who have been most occupied with the theory. Certainly the feeling that one gets from reading many of the fundamental expositions, even those of Einstein himself, is that this business of getting away from a special frame of reference and observer to something not fettered to a special point of view is very important. Yet at the same time we have to recognize that any assumed law of nature whatever can be expressed in covariant form, so that the demand for covariance by itself imposes no restriction, as was first pointed out by Kretschmann in 1917, admitted by Einstein in 1918, forgotten many times since, and emphasized again by Tolman in his book of 1934.[1] In spite, however, of Einstein's admission that covariance gives no necessary information, nevertheless the covariant expression of the "laws of nature" is put at the very bottom of the usual mathematical development for other less imperative reasons, as may be found set forth in Tolman's book. It must, I think, strike one on reflection as paradoxical to attempt to get information about nature from the requirement of covariance, for this is at bottom merely an attempt to get information about nature from an analysis of the language in terms of which we describe it, whereas the fundamental idea back of the argument as it is worked out in detail is that the sort of language with which we describe nature must be a matter of indifference.

[1] Richard C. Tolman, *Relativity, Thermodynamics, and Cosmology*, Oxford, Clarendon Press, 1934.

What is the real significance of covariance anyway, and why should it be regarded as so fundamental? What we mean by a covariant expression is one whose symbolic form is the same in every coordinate system. Tolman argues that it must be possible to express any real "law" of nature in covariant form, because if we could not, then some one coordinate system would be singled out as different from the others by the "form" of the equations, and this is not proper, because the coordinate system is a matter of no moment in describing a "natural law." But it is of course recognized that the numerical value of the coefficients must be different in different coordinate systems, so that this would afford a means of singling out a definite coordinate system in terms of any arbitrarily selected numerical coefficient. Or in general one is prompted to ask why *should not* different coordinate systems play a different part? In the last analysis the whole scheme of nature must make sense primarily to me, who am a special observer and who employ a special coordinate system. Why not carry the same argument further; what is a coordinate system except a tool for dealing with nature, and if we are to require that it is immaterial what coordinate system we use, why not require that it is immaterial what other tools we use? This would lead us in particular to inquire why there should be any special significance in the description of phenomena in terms of interval. But this of course is fundamental. It is a brute fact of experience that we have found certain procedures well adapted to the description of nature, among others the procedure for measuring interval. The fundamental thing here is a definite, unique, physical operation, which, confining ourselves to ordinary three-dimensional space for simplicity, consists of laying a straight edge between two points and observing the distance between them on the scale of the straight edge. This procedure is absolute, always the same, and not affected by my coordinate system.

The equations for $ds$ have physical content in stating that other sorts of operation beside the fundamental operation with the straight edge (as e.g. the operation of determining the difference of coordinates of the projections of the interval along Cartesian coordinate directions) can be made by proper calculation to yield the same result as the fundamental absolute operation. The physical significance of the invariance of $ds$ is merely that there is such an absolute fundamental physical procedure. Invariants of other sorts similarly find their meaning only in the existence of other sorts of physical procedure with absolute significance. Covariance seems to play no necessary part in this picture.

It cannot be too strongly emphasized that there is no getting away from preferred operations and a unique standpoint in physics; the unique physical operations in terms of which interval has its meaning afford one example, and there are many others also. There is no escaping the fact that it is *I* who have the experiences that I am trying to coordinate into a physical theory, and that *I* must be the ultimate center of any account which I can give. I and my doings must be specially set apart and, in perhaps the only possible sense of the word, constitute an absolute. It seems to me that to attempt to minimize this fact constitutes an almost wilful refusal to accept the obvious structure of experience. In so far as the general spirit of relativity theory postulates an underlying "reality" from which this aspect of experience is cancelled out, it seems to me to be palpably false, and furthermore devoid of operational meaning.

If we grant that the demand for covariance is not an essential in the argument of relativity theory, but that the same results can be obtained by other paths, as will be suggested in detail later, then we must recognize that our criticisms of the last few paragraphs apply rather to what many of its expounders have said about the theory, rather than to the theory itself as revealed by the operations which it actually employs. But leaving entirely to one side the question of covariance, the operations demanded by the equations themselves in changing coordinates involve the physical possibility of apprehending a happening in two frames of reference and describing it as the "same" in the two frames. This still involves us in all those nebulous and unsolved questions of language and meaning already suggested. Even without going as deep as questions of meaning and its communication, it would seem to me that the basic device of attempting to get information from the accounts which two observers give of a phenomenon may justly be questioned until a more searching analysis than any yet made proves that the operations in which two observers may participate are not subject to different and probably more severe restrictions than the operations permissible to only one.

The assumption that two different observers may each observe a happening and recognize it as the same involves us in particular difficulties when we proceed to very small-scale phenomena. If quantum theory is right, the ultimate elementary act of observation must be the reception and perception of a single photon, a process which by its essential nature cannot be participated in by two observers. If, then, the arguments and the underlying physical operations on which the theory rests are intrinsically incapable of being extended into the domain of very small-scale phenomena, it seems to me that one may well question whether the theory itself is applicable in this domain. There seems to be, however, a very widespread conviction among theoretical physicists that it should be possible to reconcile wave mechanics with relativity theory, at least with special relativity theory as contrasted with the general theory. It seems to be generally felt by physicists that the special theory of relativity is on an entirely different basis from the general theory.

There are several reasons for this greater confidence in the special theory. The basis for the special theory is more obviously experimental, it contains fewer philosophical considerations, and the check against experiment has been much more extensive. This has apparently led to the conviction that in special theory we have something pretty fundamental, and that any really fundamental law of nature must be invariant under a Lorentz transformation. But with regard to the particular point now under discussion the situation of the special theory is no better than that of the general theory. For the fundamental arguments of the special theory demand a light signal, thought of as expanding spherically through space and apprehended by many observers, and therefore consisting of many photons. This suggests strongly that the range of application of special theory may also be restricted to comparatively large-scale phenomena. I think it is significant that theorists of the highest ability have not effected a satisfactory reconciliation of wave mechanics and special theory after prolonged attempts. If the fundamental ideas of the two theories were really compatible, previous experience would lead us to expect that the fusion could be accomplished easily and rapidly, with the appearance of a certain inevitableness, and the prediction of a number of new experimental phenomena. Such has not been the case. In particular the experimental proofs of special relativity theory have been almost entirely restricted to large-scale phenomena, except for the explanation accepted at the present moment of certain spectroscopic fine structures and perhaps one or two others. But the fluctuating history of this fine structure situation, with its demonstration that a mathematical theory is not unique, and that a particular type of check with experiment cannot be used reversibly as a proof of the correctness of the theory that predicts it, will justify one in not ascribing any final significance to this agreement. The explanation of the success of special relativity theory on a large scale may possibly be found in some statistical effect of the combination of large numbers of quantum processes.

Returning to the relation of the general theory to small-scale phenomena, I very much question whether the general theory can successfully resist being drawn down to the level of small-scale phenomena if the reduction of all observations to pointer readings is an essential part of its argument. It is to be noticed that the reduction of observations to pointer readings plays an essential rôle not only in the argument for covariance, which may perhaps be modified or avoided, but also in the fundamental assumption that two observers may communicate with each other. For by reducing everything to pointer readings we have essentially limited every observer to the possession of the same single sense, and have thereby avoided those troublesome questions of meaning which must arise when one observer perceives tactually as heat what the other observer perceives ocularly as light. But certainly on a large scale the thesis that all measurements can be reduced to pointer readings could not be maintained, for there is no connection in direct experience, for example, between the comparison of the intensities of two illuminations in a photometer or the location of a sound by the binaural effect and a pointer reading. It can only be maintained that it is possible to analyze the situations giving rise to these sensations into a complex of simpler elements which can be adequately reproduced by pointer readings. This certainly has not yet been done, but it is perhaps not inconsistent with much that we have already accepted in physics to suppose that it could be done. The important thing, however, is that in order to prove this point we would have to carry the application of relativity theory down into small-scale things. If it should prove that we have to burrow so far down as to get into the domain of quantum phenomena, we encounter difficulties as yet unresolved.

Having now considered the implications of the various assumptions fundamental to the first postulate of general relativity theory, the postulate of covariance, let us pass on to an examination of the second fundamental postulate, the postulate of equivalence. The ordinary statement of this principle, as given in Tolman, for example, is that the laws of nature (that is, the results of any experiment performed according to definite instructions) will be the same for an observer stationary in a gravitational field or for an observer in a region free from gravitational field but moving with an acceleration equal to that of free fall in the field. The great merit of this principle is its intuitive appeal, for it checks with terrestrial experience and in particular is consistent with the observation that bodies of different mass fall with the same velocity. An observer is free to explain certain effects as arising either from the action of a gravitational field or from an acceleration of his frame of reference. Either explanation is possible as long as he does not inquire into the origin of the gravitational field or of the acceleration. If he inquires into the origin of the field, or the acceleration, he loses some of his freedom of choice. If he describes himself as being in a field, he must demand that there be bodies somewhere which will account for the entire field that he assumes, or if he prefers to describe himself as accelerated, he must either discover somewhere a rope or its equivalent capable of giving the assumed acceleration to his frame of reference, or else his law of gravitation must take the curious form that there is an intrinsic gravitational field with no heavy bodies to give rise to it. Variations from this intrinsic field, however, are to be attributed to the presence of matter. When once the observer has made his choice at any particular locality as to what explanation he shall adopt for his local findings, the equations which are set up in accord with this principle can be integrated to cover the entire universe so that the account which he may thereafter give at any other place is thereby fixed. The effects at any other place are now to be described as due to a combination in definite proportions of a determinate gravitational field and a determinate acceleration. One may get some curious and complicated results in this way, particularly in rotational systems. Hence it would appear that the originally plausible and simple principle of equivalence as judged by a single local observer loses its simplicity and therefore to a large extent its plausibility when one tries to find some physical reason for the assumed gravitational or accelerational field or to extend the principle to all other localities. It seems to me that this awkwardness in attempting to extend the principle of equivalence to cover the entire universe perhaps suggests that the general theory not only must not be applied to too small-scale phenomena, but also must be limited to not too large regions, and that, in particular, we may expect trouble when it is extended to the entire universe.

There are other still more general considerations which demand, I think, that at least in the present development of critical analysis we view with serious misgivings any attempt to set up any theory applicable to the entire universe. The very concepts in terms of which we think acquire their meaning only in terms of the assumption of the possibility of indefinitely repeating experiments under identical conditions and of an observer external to and independent of the system. Both of these assumptions are obviously inapplicable to the entire universe. Furthermore, the various nebulous assumptions which we have already had to make about the possibility of communicating meaning from one observer to another seem to have had their inspiration in a narrow range of experience. It would therefore appear that at present conceptual machinery is not in existence applicable to the problem of the entire universe. Once the idea has "got under one's skin" that there are essential limitations to what the human intellect can tackle, and that here is one of the most obvious examples, I think that any attempt to set up a theory of the entire cosmos will appear to be of such exclusively anthropomorphic significance as even to divest the whole enterprise of its ostensible interest. From a more narrowly technical standpoint, one may well question the significance of making such perfectly prodigious extrapolations of any theory whose fundamental concepts have the least hint of vagueness.

How is it then, if the arguments on which the general theory rests are open to these criticisms, that the theory has given correct results, and in particular led to correct predictions with regard to the advance of the perihelion of Mercury, the displacement of the apparent position of a star in the neighborhood of the sun's disc, and the displacement of radiation emitted in a gravitational field toward the infra red? As I have already emphasized, what the theory *says* about itself is not pertinent, and an incorrect argument may lead to the same demands that other less objectionable arguments might lead to.

This, it seems to me, is what has happened here. I have tried to analyze in my *Logic of Modern Physics* what I believe has actually happened. The demand for covariance gives nothing necessary, but what is slipped into the argument during its detailed application, namely the demand for simplicity, does. For the demand for mathematical simplicity means, as it is worked out, the demand that the equations in generalized coordinates be linear, of the second order, and that they reduce to the ordinary equations under proper conditions. These assumptions about the nature of the fundamental equations are equivalent to the assumption that even in the presence of gravitational fields there are propagation phenomena like those of ordinary experience, that the principle of superposition holds, so that two causes acting simultaneously produce the sum of the effects separately, and that there is a scalar energy function. These assumptions are certainly entirely different in spirit from the original assumptions of covariance, etc., and it seems to me that these are what are actually involved if one analyzes the actual manipulations of the theory. These assumptions will not trouble the average physicist as being improbable, and he might even be willing to bet in advance on the basis of his past experience that they would be applicable in the next stage of the approximation as we extend the range of measurements.

Mathematically the essence of the situation seems to be that we have demanded that our equations be simple. Simplicity is entirely a relative matter; what may be simple from the point of view of a general formula, written out with an array of superscripts and subscripts, need not be at all simple when expanded, as one may see from the three and one-half pages of Tolman where are written out the detailed expressions for the Christoffel symbols and the components of the energy tensor associated with a simple line element which is written symbolically in half a line. Even from the mathematical point of view simplicity of form of the differential equation is not all that is required for complete simplicity; a differential equation must always have associated with it a set of boundary conditions, and a solution has to satisfy both equations and boundary conditions. It certainly gave me pause when I was informed by competent mathematicians that it is not known even whether a solution of the differential equations *exists* capable of meeting the boundary conditions for the problem of two particles. Hence the whole structure, differential equations plus boundary conditions, is not simple even in the mathematical sense, but is terribly complicated.

The situation is still worse from an experimental point of view, for there need be no connection between mathematical and experimental simplicity, as is well brought out by an elementary situation in special relativity theory. Experimentally the simplest way of measuring the length of a moving object would doubtless be to lay the meter stick on the object, mark the position of the ends, and then move it along, precisely as in measuring a stationary object. But mathematically this is not so easy to describe as another operation using the entirely unfamiliar physical instrument of a fixed coordinate system. The mathematical definition prevailed, which doubtless is at the bottom of many common intuitive difficulties with the theory. It seems to me that the experimental physicist would call only that theory simple which gives simple expression to the results of his simple physical manipulations, or which provides simple answers to some of the simple questions which he could formulate in terms of such simple physical procedures. But the mathematical theory is incapable of describing in simple terms the energy flow in such a simple system as two gravitating bodies moving with constant velocity at a fixed distance apart. The most elementary considerations show that there must be an energy flow in the gravitational field through empty space across from one body to the other; that is, there must be a gravitational analogue of the Poynting vector. We are told from the general theory that although such a vector doubtless exists, it is so complicated that it is impossible to calculate it, much less to visualize it. If this be simplicity, God help the experimental physicist. I cannot help wondering whether it would not be rewarding to attempt a fundamentally different theory of gravitational action, starting from such simple physical systems as just suggested, and postulating that there be some simple and measurable physical phenomenon in such cases. It may well be too small to measure on our ordinary scale, but it might lead to something measurable on the cosmic scale.

Summarizing the whole situation with regard to the general theory, it may well be that the few specific results and the detailed equations may stand, at least as first approximations and for large-scale phenomena, but it seems to me that the arguments which have led up to the theory and the whole state of mind of most physicists with regard to it may some day become one of the puzzles of history. The arguments, I believe, clearly involve an uncritical acceptance of many of those traditional methods of thought which we are just beginning to discover are not universally applicable.

# VIII. MATHEMATICAL MODELS AND PROBABILITY

W E have seen that recent theoretical physics makes use of mathematical models instead of the physical models of classical theory. The fundamental requirement in a mathematical model is that it shall serve as a calculating device, from which we may compute the answer to any question regarding the physical behavior of the corresponding physical system. Since the experimental accuracy with which any measurement can be made is limited, we cannot expect to check with complete precision the demands of any mathematical model. It is conceivable that two formally quite different models might give numerical results which were the same within the errors of experiment, but which differed in higher order terms. Under these conditions either model would serve equally well as a calculating device, and we would have to choose between them on other grounds, usually on the ground of convenience or of ease of calculation, or of simplicity in the argument by which the model was set up.

The argument is almost always arranged so that the steps in the development are given a ring of physical plausibility. It is felt not to be good form to introduce features into the mathematical model for the sole purpose of providing the correct answer, but some other justification is felt to be necessary. This may lead to interesting situations. Thus Lorentz[1] has pointed out that gravitational action between bodies can be accounted for if we assume a slight difference in the electric force between equal positive and negative charges, so that there is a resultant force between two electrically neutral bodies. It is possible by a proper adjustment of the constant

[1] H. A. Lorentz, *Proc. Kon. Akad. Amst.*, 2, 559, 1900.

determining the difference between the action of the two sorts of charge to reproduce the gravitational constant, and it was shown by Lorentz that the change in the law of force between elementary charges necessary to do this is so slight that it is forever beyond reach of any possible experiment on electrical forces, and that it could be detected only by the ordinary gravitational experiments.

This sort of theory would not at one time have been thought permissible unless the fundamental postulates should be verified by experiment, for it was felt that there was no essential limit to the accuracy with which any sort of physical measurement might some day be made, so that when that day arrived the assumption as to whether the law of force was correct or not would become capable of an answer yes or no. But now that it is realized that there are essential limitations to the accuracy with which certain kinds of physical measurement can be made it may become physically meaningless to seek an answer to whether such microscopic modifications in the law of force are correct or not by direct determinations of the law of force, and the only meaning that can be found is in the indirect consequences.

Suppose that all the indirect consequences that can be verified by experiment are so verified, shall we then say that the fundamental assumption is true? I think we would be hesitant to apply the word truth to this situation, even if all possible experimental checks were met, because truth always carries, by traditional usage, the further implication of uniqueness. As long as we were uncertain whether there might not be some other assumption about the elementary action which would lead to the same measurable results, I think we would not be willing to say that our particular assumption was "true." That is, here is a situation to which all the implications of "true" do not apply, and it is meaningless to say of a particular assumption that it must be either true or false. The concept of not-true, or false, still applies, because if we can show that any of the indirect consequences are opposed to experiment, then the assumption is false. But the concept of true is not applicable. I think we would want to invent a new concept to cover this situation; probably the word "possible" has enough of the required connotations to meet our needs, and we can say that the assumption about the elementary forces is a possible assumption (with a slightly altered meaning for the word possible) if all the possible experimental checks are met but uniqueness cannot be proved.

It seems to me that the discovery of inherent limitations to the accuracy of physical measurements disclosed by wave mechanics opens the door to a flood of "possible" theories. I can see no legitimate argument by which any theory built on the same general plan as Lorentz's may be summarily dismissed, as many physicists are inclined to dismiss it, or any justification for denying physical "reality" to the assumptions of such a theory. The assumptions have all the physical reality that can have any operational meaning in the circumstances. The conclusion, of course, is that the concept of physical reality has to be modified in the realm of construction beyond the reach of accurate measurement, and in particular, that reality can no longer connote uniqueness.

We are thus faced with a radically new situation which may well alter the entire future of theory building. Doubtless a great many alternative theories will be possible, and we shall have to choose between them on grounds of simplicity or convenience of calculation or perhaps on purely esthetic considerations. It may be that one type of theory will prove to be simple and convenient when dealing with certain aspects of phenomena, while a radically different theory may prove better for other aspects. We have a suggestion of this sort of thing in relativity theory, where one procedure is mathematically simplest for measuring the length of a moving object, whereas an entirely different procedure is simplest physically. Under such circumstances we would be foolish to stick to a single type of theory for all uses, in the idea that only one theory could be the "right" theory. I suspect that Bohr, with his dual aspects of reality, is one of the first to exploit this possibility. The celebrated remark of Sir William Bragg that we seem forced to use classical mechanics on Monday, Wednesday and Friday, and wave mechanics on Tuesday, Thursday, and Saturday may prove not to be a reductio ad absurdum, as it is usually taken to be, but an ultimate and necessary procedure.

Our attitude toward the question of "emergent" properties, which has been much discussed lately, particularly by biologists, is somewhat altered by our recognition of these new possibilities in the way of theory building. What one understands by "emergence" is the possession of properties by a large assemblage of elements which are not determined solely by the properties of the elements taken as individuals; that is, the combination contributes something essentially new. It is a common thesis among biologists that the organism as a combination of cells has properties not latent in the properties of the individual cells. What now is the precise physical meaning of such a thesis?

It can only mean that an exhaustive experimental study of the properties of the individual cells discloses no property from which can be deduced the necessity of some of the properties that are displayed by an aggregate of many cells. But what do we mean by "deduced"? Deduction involves some type of theory. Because of the inherent limited accuracy of physical measurements we must now admit the possibility of many different kinds of theory of the same physical phenomenon. There would seem to be no reason why some of these theories, perhaps by the same device as Lorentz's of postulating properties of the elements which are physically meaningless, because not capable of direct experimental verification, but mathematically real because they vitally affect the nature of the mathematical theory, should not be capable of "deducing" the presumed emergent properties. The properties would then by definition cease to be emergent. On the other hand, there might well be other theories which do not ascribe to the elements mathematical properties which have no physical significance, but introduce as an explicit postulate that combinations of many elements give something essentially new. Such a theory would represent the property in question as truly emergent. There would be no operational method of choosing one type of theory in preference to the other. That is, the whole question of "emergence" seems to lose any aspect of physical "reality" and to reduce to a matter of convention, determined primarily by considerations of simplicity and convenience. In any event, without exploiting the new possibilities in the way of theory building, it would seem to me that our recognition that the operational meaning of "emergence" involves a deduction by some theory is sufficient to show that "emergence" of itself cannot have physical reality. Physical reality can be ascribed to emergence only in a setting which includes the type of theory to be used in the deduction.

All these infelicities are obviously the direct result of the fact that our mathematics is not so constructed that it automatically ceases to be valid in the range of magnitudes so small as to have no physical meaning.

We have been talking about the behavior of mathematical models in the region beyond direct verification by experiment, and in particular in the region of things too small to measure. We can also get beyond the range of measurement by going to very large things, or by extrapolating to very large positive or negative values of time. If we go to very large things, we make theories of the cosmos, which we will discuss presently. In the direction of large times we may also run into cosmic theories; we also run into certain situations of statistical mechanics in this direction. Particularly instructive situations are presented by statistical mechanics and the theory of probabilities. It is usual in discussing the deductions of the second law of thermodynamics or of the meaning of entropy from the statistical point of view to emphasize that on the basis of statistical mechanics unfamiliar configurations of a system are not impossible, but only improbable. One may even compute how many years one may expect to have to wait to see a pail of water freeze on the fire. What physical meaning shall we give to the result of this calculation? The result is of course such a large number of years as to forever discourage any thought of a direct experimental verification; we content ourselves with a very rough and qualitative check on the plausibility of our result by remarking that such an event has never been observed to occur, and that our calculation shows that in all the time of past recorded observations such an event would have been exceedingly improbable. The improbability is so high, however, that we can accept the merely negative results of observation as lending only a very weak plausibility to the "truth" of the calculation. The meaning of the "truth" of such a calculation must be sought in other directions. If we could show that the conclusion followed necessarily by logical processes from the assumptions that went into the deduction, and if we could show that the assumptions were true physically by some sort of operational test, then I think we would be willing to call the conclusion "true." Among the assumptions that went into the deduction were the laws of mechanics. It can be shown that these would have to hold with a very high degree of precision indeed, a precision fantastically beyond any possible experimental verification, in order to demand the conclusion. Hence we are not justified in saying that our mathematical theory requires us to believe that the freezing of a pail of water on the fire at rare intervals is a necessary feature of our universe. I believe that this sort of situation holds in general and I have tried to make plausible in a paper on statistical mechanics[2] that it is impossible to deduce rigorously by the methods of statistical mechanics the probable occurrence of events so rare that they have not yet ever been observed. If one takes any special satisfaction in such a procedure, I can see no reason why he should not assume small variations in the laws of mechanics, specially and arbitrarily constructed so as to rule out just these rare occurrences, and no one can deny that such is a "possible" theory if it leads into no measurable conflict with experiment.

It may be asked, why lay so much emphasis on these rare occurrences? Even if the theory does allow rare occurrences, which we do not like to associate with the physical system, has not the model done all that can be required of it if it checks with experience in the measurable range? I think this position is the proper one. It happens, however, that the model is often used by extrapolation far beyond the range of possible experimental verification, and of course the kind of extrapolation that one gets does depend enormously on the precise form of the fundamental assumptions. If one uses the results of these extrapolations in his speculations we may then have the anomalous situation that the entire course of the speculation may hinge on differences in the fundamental assumptions so minute that it is meaningless to ask whether they are true or not. A very striking example is afforded by speculations about the "heat death." If the laws of mechanics held with mathematical precision then there is a finite probability that any configuration whatever, no matter how far removed from the most probable, will occur. The usual argument now is that the former state of the universe, with small

[2] "Statistical Mechanics and the Second Law of Thermodynamics," *Bull. Amer. Math. Soc.*, April, 1932.

entropy, from which we are evidently proceeding in the direction of increasing entropy, may therefore merely have been a state reached by chance fluctuations, and therefore may be a state that will recur in the future. In this way the dilemma of the "heat death" can be avoided. But one can attach no operational meaning to the question of whether such an explanation is "true" or not. Of course one can have no quarrel with the interest which one may find in working out all the logical consequences of a set of hypotheses, but it seems to me that in this field there is particular danger that some of the implications may be improper implications unless one takes the greatest care with his analysis.

The sort of consideration brought up by the heat death is typical of what we encounter whenever we are driven to use the methods of probability. The operational background which gives meaning to the concepts of probability is so different from the operational background of ordinary experience that even the same sort of language does not apply to it, and we are constantly in danger of making errors if we apply the same language, as we are often strongly tempted to do.

It is a matter of experience that there are typical and recognizable situations in which no method has been discovered for predicting what is going to happen next, such, for example, as calling the toss of a coin. In spite of the fact that we cannot predict, we are under the inner necessity for planning some course of conduct when confronted with such situations. Whenever possible we plan our actions so that they can meet all possible contingencies, as when we take light and heavy clothing on a journey in order to provide against the uncertainties of weather. But some situations cannot be met in this way, but have to be met by unique action. For example, I may be asked to bet on whether the next two throws of a coin will be two heads or two tails, or one head and one tail.

If the betting is even, why is it, that if I am well informed, I will invariably bet on one head and one tail? Of course I bet this way because the "chance" for a head and a tail is better than for either of the other two possible events.

What is this "chance" that I ascribe to the event? It is to be noted in the first place that this "chance" is not a property of the event by itself in the ordinarily used sense of "property," for when the event has once occurred there is no operational procedure by which I can check whether the chance was actually what I thought it was. I believe that the only operational meaning that can be given to chance or probability referred to an individual event is with respect to my frame of mind when deciding on a course of action in anticipation of the event. "Probability" as a "property" which has meaning in terms of physical operations is a term not applicable to the individual event, but is applicable only to an individual event plus a setting. The setting is the repetition of the event under identical conditions a great many times. The reason that we deal with the situation in this way is that we have discovered by experience that the event in the setting of many repetitions does have certain regularities which allow us to attain a certain measure of success with predictions of a certain sort. That is, it is a matter of experience that events unpredictable by themselves may have certain statistical regularities in large numbers, and the operational meaning of physical probability is to be found in the nature of these statistical regularities. Thus the probability is one-half for a head if in a long series of throws the ratio of the number of heads to total throws is approximately one-half. But how long must be the series of throws and how closely must the ratio approach one-half? There is no definite answer: we can only say that the more throws the better. Let us suppose that I have thrown all day, until I am tired, and have found a ratio 0.4995 between the two numbers. I then ask, "Is this good enough, and can I be sure that the probability is one-half?" The answer has to be: "No, you cannot be quite sure, the probability might have been ten to one in favor of tails, only it 'chanced' by rare bad luck that you got a long string of nearly equal numbers." So we have to admit that we can never be sure that the concept of probability applies *at all* in any given situation, or in fact we cannot be sure that the concept of probability has ever applied to any of the situations in that past that we have treated by this method. The nature of the concept is such that it can never be proved correct, but in its own construction it must leave room for the possibility that it may be incorrect. We have here a paradox: what theory is it that is not correct unless it leaves open the possibility that it may be incorrect? Answer: the theory of probability.

This is a sort of situation that makes us uncomfortable; it seems to suggest that the logical processes of the human intellect are not capable of meeting all the situations with which they are confronted in practice. We have no doubt by now recognized that we were not always successful in meeting exactly the physical situations of experience, and we are rather sure that this must be one of them.

It is most difficult to resist attaching to the verbiage of probability the implications of ordinary language. For example, imagine our young friend asking our advice on how he shall bet on the next two throws of a coin: we advise him to bet a head and a tail. "Why?" he asks. "Because you are surer of getting the right answer that way than any other," we reply. "Are you sure of that?" he asks. "Yes," we reply. The coin is thrown, two heads come up, and our friend loses. "What did you mean," he asks, "by saying that a head and a tail were surer of coming up than anything else—something else did come up—prove to me that what you said was true." "Oh," say we, "of course what we meant was that if you bet a great many times, you would have been right oftener that way than any other." "But I couldn't bet a great many times; I had money for only one bet, and you knew it, and now I have lost it." "Oh, in that case there was nothing we could have done for you," we reply. "Then why did you advise me?" he retorts. Why indeed—or why indeed do we advise *ourselves* as to what we shall do in such situations? The answer is largely an answer of despair, we have to do something and there is naught else to do. Our only possible method of meeting the future is on the basis of past experience; we have observed that more of our fellows have successfully met the situations in which they have been caught by acting according to the theory than by acting in any other way, and accordingly we decide to meet the next situation in the same way too, although we know perfectly well that this mode of action has no pertinence with respect to the next situation, but is pertinent only when applied to an aggregate of many situations. Even then, it is not exactly pertinent, and what is more, I may not even survive the next situation to play again. That is, we have not been successful in meeting our environment here. By hypothesis we cannot be successful, but we act nevertheless even although we do not anticipate success. In the end we come to refuse to admit our failure even to ourselves, and talk about such situations with the language of ordinary experience applicable to situations which have been successfully met.

Although we cannot apply the notions of probability with rigor to any actual situation, we can nevertheless play a rigorous mathematical game with the notions of probability, and in particular ascribe a definite probability to any compound event in our game, meaning merely that the probability of this compound event will be calculated from the probability of other simple events according to definite mathematical rules. Thus if I say that the probability of throwing tails three times in succession is ⅛, I am simply solving a certain *mathematical* problem with regard to a sequence of three *mathematical* events, the probability of each of which individually is by *definition* one-half.

What is involved when I treat by the mathematical theory of probability any physical system, such as the gas under the advancing piston of a gas engine? In the first place, as we have already seen, I erect a model, containing particles which are the counterpart of the molecules of the actual gas; in this respect my model is to be a physical model. Each of these particles is further endowed with certain of the properties which have experimental meaning when applied to actual particles, namely velocity. Collisions take place between the particles which alter the velocities. The way in which the velocities of two colliding particles are altered depends on the relative positions of the centers of mass at the moment of impact, and on other parameters of the molecules. If the particles are replaced by hard elastic spheres, then it is possible to calculate exactly the velocity after collision in terms of the velocities before collision and relative positions of centers on impact. If now we imagine a great many such collisions, and further suppose that the relative positions of the points of impact are distributed at random, we can calculate the frequency with which all possible relative velocities will be found after the collision. The calculation involves the ability to calculate in complete detail the result of any specified collision, but in virtue of our assumption of random distribution of the points of impact, we cannot predict where or when any particular type of collision takes place. After collision we pick out from all the possible resulting pairs a particular particle for further analysis, and discuss again what happens when it collides with some other particle coming from another collision. We assign relative numbers to the different types of collisions and the different possible resultants on the basis of the "probabilities," and the result of the analysis is to show that certain properties of the system as a whole are conserved, and that uniformities tend to become established in the mean of other properties, and these are found to have a parallel in the behavior of the actual gas. The assumption of *random* distribution of the points of impact at the instant of collision is merely saying in other words that all relative positions are equally *probable,* that is, the notion of probability has to be introduced as a postulate in describing the behavior of the actual physical system. But this we have seen is meaningless under these conditions; the notion of probability does not apply to concrete physical situations. The distribution of the relative positions of the points of impact is not random in any particular gas, but is quite definite and discoverable by exact measurement (at least in principle as far as kinetic theory is concerned). We cannot logically assign probability properties to any actual physical system, and in so doing for purposes of calculation we have reduced our model from a physical model to a mathematical model. We have here a sort of hybrid, a model in which the elementary particles purport to have their counterpart in the physical system, but which are treated in a way which has no immediate physical significance. But the result which we obtain in this way does have physical significance, because it reproduces the behavior of the actual physical system.

We will doubtless try to justify by some sort of argument our expectation of success with a procedure of this sort. Perhaps our argument might run as follows: "We have studied a large number of concrete special cases in which the method of distribution is exactly given and we have found, when the situation is as complex as here, that we can never discover any uniformities in the method of distribution such as would lead to the expectation of any particular notable type of behavior after the collisions." This reply, of course, is only a polite lie, but perhaps our catechizer will grant some justification for our optimistic feeling that we might actually prove the correctness of our statement if given time enough, and will content himself merely with asking what types of regularity in the behavior after collisions we have excluded by these considerations? I think we would be forced to reply that we have excluded those which appear simple to us from the point of view of the calculations that we are competent to make. "And why," our examiner would doubtless proceed, "do you attach particular physical significance just to those types of regularity?" To which we would probably reply after long consideration that it must be regarded as an essential part of the theory that just those types of regularity have physical significance. To which our examiner would doubtless retort, "Oh," and drop the matter. But he might go back to our original reply, and ask us how we selected the original concrete special cases which we had favored with our detailed examination.

We would doubtless emerge from our encounter with the examiner in a thoughtful and probably somewhat dissatisfied mood. I think we would eventually give up our line of defense as untenable, and admit that we cannot put this thing on a strictly logical basis, but must make a fresh appeal to experiment. It is a brute fact that we have been successful in handling by the methods of probability many systems composed of large numbers in which the relations between the elements are so complex that we have been able to discover no regularity by the methods of analysis at our command. I think that in the last analysis we cannot ask *why* our probability methods have been successful in treating such systems, for I do not believe that any possible answer can be given in logically rigorous form, because the fundamental notion of probability itself cannot be made completely rigorous. If we cannot ask *why* our probability methods are successful, we may well question the exact status of any "explanation" of physical behavior which we obtain by such means. Apparently we must accept our ability to treat actual physical systems by probability methods as another empirical discovery. We can never escape the implications of the fact that our actual experience is lived only once, and consists of a succession of actual concrete situations. How can we expect to treat such systems with complete rigor by means of a concept which by definition is never applicable to any concrete event, but by construction is applicable only to a fictitious aggregate of many?

It is true that by much experience we have come to have an intuitive feeling for situations in which the probability method will give us the correct answer, and in fact the intuitive recognition is made so easily that we can take a genuine satisfaction in such an analysis, for example, as that which describes the increase of entropy of a system as a progress from a less probable to a more probable configuration. But always somewhere in the background is lurking an application of the mathematical idea of probability to an actual physical system. We may push the place where probability has to be assumed more and more into the remote background, but we never get rid of it, and it always plays an essential rôle.

Consider, for example, a gas enclosed in solid walls; at any instant the motion of the gas is not random but definite, and it has a definite sequence. What prevents the following out through all future time of a definite sequence is the walls, the atoms of which are supposed to be in such a complex state of motion, because they are in connection with the entire outer universe and to a certain extent reflect its complexities, that no resultant regularities are *to be expected* in the motion which the atoms of the wall impress on the atoms of the gas.

But the entire outer universe is probably finite; why then can we say "No resultant regularities are to be expected"? I think our expectation can only be put on an empirical basis. In describing what this empirical basis is we might go so far as to admit complete defeat by saying that our expectation is based on the fact that our observation shows that the second law of thermodynamics describes the behavior of nature. Or we may not be willing to relinquish a claim to having actually put things in a somewhat new light, and we might then describe the empirical basis by some sort of a paraphrase of what we actually do in appealing to experiment. It strikes me that the following is a rather illuminating paraphrase: "We find by experience that our conventional physical tools, meaning thereby instruments and concepts, are adequate to deal with our large-scale physical experience in the sense that out of no situation which is so complex as to defy analysis into simpler constituents by these tools do details ever develop which are coarse enough to be analyzed by these same tools." That is, if our thermometers and pressure gauges cannot detect measurable inequalities in the original condition of the gas or its walls, then at later instants we never find inequalities detectible by these same thermometers and pressure gauges which we could explain by assuming in the initial system the existence of inequalities too small to detect. On a given scale of magnitude, inequalities do not grow but tend to smooth out.

The kinetic theory of gases which thus rests on a logically incomplete basis seems to make as good connection with experiment as other more logical theories, so that it seems to be possible as a matter of fact to deal with actual situations by methods which are not capable of complete logical rigor. It would appear therefore that perhaps we were going too far when we set up complete logical rigor as the tacit ideal toward which any rational intellectual process should strive.

It may be that there is such a thing as successive approximations in the approach to complete self-consistency—that in making connection with experience we may be able to construct such mental devices that any self-contradictions which they may involve will be permanently confined to the realm of constructions, beyond the reach of direct experiment. I think the reaction of the practical physicist to all this criticism of ours of the theory of probability—a shrug of the shoulders and the unexpressed thought that it really does not matter—is, after all, of significance. It shows that anyone familiar with practical situations instinctively realizes that sufficiently good results can be got with imperfect tools. Since there is no meaning in asking whether results more than just "sufficiently" good are not in closer touch with "reality," it would seem that we may not have had a perfectly clear perception of the necessary characteristics of thought. We have perhaps been going too far in talking about the "laws of thought" as though they had mathematical precision.

Considerations similar to those which we have just applied to probability theory apply to certain aspects of the general problem of cosmogony. To me the most striking thing about cosmogony is the perfectly hair-raising extrapolations which it is necessary to make. We have to extend to times of the order of $10^{13}$ years and distances of the order of $10^9$ light years laws which have been checked in a range of not more than $3 \times 10^2$ years, and certainly in distances not greater than the distance which the solar system has travelled in that time, or about $4 \times 10^{-2}$ light years. It seems to me that one cannot take such extrapolations seriously unless one subscribes to a metaphysics that claims that laws of the necessary mathematical precision *really* control the actual physical universe. For such a metaphysical claim I can find no operational meaning that would give one the slightest confidence in applying it in any concrete situation. Here again one encounters essential limitations. The only operational meaning of remote epochs of time or of great distances is to be sought in what we do here and now—either in our present actions or our present program and expectations for the future. From the operational point of view, therefore, cosmogony must be an essentially different sort of thing from the activity of the terrestrial physicist in his laboratory.

Some of these differences I have pointed out in an article entitled "The Nature and Limitations of Cosmical Inquiries,"[3] and it is not necessary to give the arguments again in detail. This article has made an unfortunate impression on some readers; they have found the criticisms captious, and have felt that it puts the astronomer in an unfavorable light because it suggests that he is not fully aware of what he is doing and is to a certain extent a victim of self-deception, whereas he could not proceed any differently even if he wanted to. My main purpose in writing the article was to bring out into the light of full self-consciousness a vivid realization that there are essential differences of meaning between the concepts of the cosmogonist and the ordinary experimental physicist, in spite of the fact that both use the same language. What the consequences of such a realization will be in any individual must be more or less a personal matter. I cannot help feeling, however, that when a realization of the essential difference of meaning has actually "got under one's skin," there must be shifts of interest, and that programs which might have been interesting under the old connotations now lose their appeal. It seems to me that in view of the programs which are of interest to active cosmogonists it is not unfair to surmise that an awareness of the essential difference of meanings has not "got under the skin" of all astronomers.

[3] *Scientific Monthly*, 37, 385, 1933.

# IX. WAVE MECHANICS

WE NOW attempt some critical appraisal of certain aspects of modern wave mechanics—what is its object —what does it have in common with any possible physical theory—how successful is it? In this discussion we shall not be concerned with the historical steps in the development of the theory, but consider only the actual structure as we now have it. Neither shall we concern ourselves at all with the success of wave mechanics in meeting the situations for which it was specially designed, but recognize without question that its success has been brilliantly greater than that of any other theory in solving the problems of atomic physics, a success which doubtless means a long continued usefulness for its methods, just as Newtonian mechanics still retains its indispensable field of usefulness. We shall rather be concerned with some of the more general aspects of the theory, and with its ability to coordinate everything under a single point of view.

In one very important respect quantum theory is able to give a more faithful reproduction of the qualitative character of experience than any theory which preceded it. This success appears not to have been the result of deliberate design, but was a more or less incidental by-product of the fundamental mathematical mechanism. Practically all former theories have had such a mathematical structure as to suggest that the necessary physical measurements were capable of limitless precision. This pretense on the part of the older theories of course deceived no one, and it was recognized that any conclusions of such theories could have validity only within the accuracy of the measurements. The effect of inaccuracies in the measurements had to be allowed for in various clumsy ways—these methods were never very explicitly discussed, and were the sort of thing that had to be included in what we have called the "text" which always accompanies the formal mathematical part of the theory. I suppose that even before the days of wave mechanics anyone would probably have guessed that experimental error of some sort would always be present, although there might appear to be no reason why its magnitude might not be indefinitely reduced. A particular kind of error that would have had to be included was error arising, not from imperfections in the physical measuring apparatus, but from imperfections in the observer. Every observer knows that he occasionally makes errors for which he can give no account afterward, and he can see no method of completely getting rid of such blunders. It might have been realized, therefore, even before wave mechanics, that all the conventional mathematical theories failed of complete success in reproducing the actual situation because they gave no recognition, as an integral part of the theory, to the inevitable presence of error of one kind or another. Wave mechanics, on the other hand, does have a place, in virtue of its fundamental mathematical construction, for an uncertainty which is qualitatively the sort of thing that might arise from error, as, for example, the lack of sharpness when we try to measure simultaneously position and momentum. It represents this uncertainty as an intrinsic element in the situation, not to be avoided. In thus providing a mechanism for the automatic inclusion of something akin to error, wave mechanics gives itself the possibility of getting qualitatively closer to experience in this vital respect than classical mechanics ever could.

What is the method by which wave mechanics has succeeded in reproducing this qualitative aspect of experience, and what are its intrinsic limitations, for limitations of some sort there always are? Wave mechanics obtains this objective by a specific mechanism and definite hypothesis. It is almost forced to be thus specific because of the character of the formal mathematics which is always used in physical theory; this is incapable of dealing with situations purely qualitatively, but can use only definite quantitative language. The inherent necessity of there always being error is secured by the device of reducing everything to a basis of probability. The numerical limitations of this intrinsic probability appear in a new constant, $h$, which determines the necessary scale of the lack of sharpness. Because of the mathematical necessity of introducing this constant, we have to go far beyond the original physical recognition that error must always be present, and have to set up the thesis that the irreducible error enters in a certain peculiar way determined by the behavior of conjugate quantities, and furthermore that it can never be reduced below a certain definite value. This value is so far beyond present experimental possibilities that it is at present without physical meaning to inquire whether the hypothesis of a finite inherent error in the measurement of certain elemental things is "correct" or not. Historically, of course, the constant $h$ was not introduced to ensure the presence of error as a qualitative factor, but $h$ was introduced to explain other experimental effects and it was later found that more or less incidentally error was at the same time provided for.

Although wave mechanics presents us with a structure which has some of the qualitative features of error, examination shows that the correspondence is not in all respects as close as we could wish. For wave mechanics admits certain sorts of quantities which may be known with indefinite precision, which certainly does not correspond to experience, and on the other hand admits in those quantities which cannot be measured with indefinite precision the occasional appearance of indefinitely great divergencies from the expected values, for which again there is no more warrant in experience than for the freezing of water on the fire. Neither is there any possibility for the elimination of suspected blunders on the part of the observer by the method of check by repetition. The assumption of the possibility that some measurements may be indefinitely repeated is almost a prerequisite to the very meaning of error in the ordinary sense, whereas in wave mechanics it is only in exceptional circumstances that we can put ourselves in a position to repeat a measurement exactly. It would thus appear that error is a different sort of thing in wave mechanics than in our inherited way of thinking. It is a question for examination whether our inherited ideas of error may be so modified as to retain their really essential characteristics and at the same time be consistent with the demands of the mathematical theory, but so far as I know the examination has not been made and the result cannot be safely assumed in advance.

We may grant, however, that although it has not been as successful as we could wish, and that the result was attained more or less incidentally, nevertheless wave mechanics is able to achieve a degree of qualitative agreement with experience which had not been possible with previous theories, and we must recognize this as an important advance.

This advance has involved introducing the notion of probability as an *elemental* assumption of the theory. Hitherto it has been a legitimate task for physical theory to "explain" why it is possible to reproduce approximately the behavior of certain aggregates of large numbers in terms of the laws of probability. These "explanations" we have seen not to be particularly cogent, mostly on account of a necessary failure of logical rigor in the fundamental notions of probability itself, but the mind has nevertheless apparently got a certain satisfaction out of explanations of this character, and, what is more, has been able to use them with profit. But to accept probability as an ultimate, and thus to give up the possibility

of explaining its appearance, is a drastic reversal of previous
ideals, and involves, among other things, the abandonment
of a completely deterministic attitude. It puts no intolerable
burden on our powers of intellectual adaptation to be forced
to abandon this attitude, as has been shown in many dis-
cussions of the significance of the Heisenberg principle of
indetermination. Furthermore, the indirect consequences of
such an assumption have been experimentally verified in a
great number of cases. Nevertheless I feel that there is still
room for experiments specially designed to test the direct
applicability of these assumptions on the most minute scale
possible to reach, and in particular, room for experiments
designed to test the distribution of error on the small scale. A
number of years ago I published a list of simple questions,[1]
the answer to which it seemed to me would involve a closer
knowledge of elemental things than we then had. I think
it would still be difficult to find the answer to some of these
questions, and I believe that there are still significant possibilities for experiment here.

The introduction of probability as an unanalyzable in
modern wave mechanics has other important consequences
besides the abandonment of a completely deterministic attitude. We have seen that the notion of probability is never
applicable to any actual individual physical situation, and
in fact cannot be exactly applicable even to a finite collection
of such systems. The ensemble of systems, to which only probability rigorously applies, is not a physical ensemble, which
is always finite, but again is only a mathematical ensemble.
The theory is thus unavoidably a theory of the *mathematical
model*.

The mathematical model aspect of wave mechanics is particularly obvious if one considers the rôle played by the
boundary conditions. In ordinary classical theory the differen-

[1] "Permanent Elements in the Flux of Present-Day Physics," *Science,* 71, 19, 1930.

tial equations by themselves have a definite physical significance in describing the properties of the medium, as in
elasticity theory for example, so that it was possible to deduce
the differential equation from a knowledge of the physical
properties of the medium. The boundary conditions then
represented something physical in addition that could be
superposed on the medium. But in the wave equation of
Schrödinger this separation cannot be made, for it is only
the complex of differential equations plus boundary conditions which have a physical counterpart. For example, in
many situations only discrete values of energy are allowed
because other values demand one kind or another of an "infinite catastrophe." The classical method of interpretation
would suggest that for such energy values something special
would occur in the system, such perhaps as becoming un-
stable and passing to an essentially different configuration.
But since such situations are known not to occur physically,
we just say that that part of the mathematics has no physical
counterpart, at least without altering the original physical
set-up. We are not allowed to ask "why" that part of the
mathematics does not correspond, or "why" it is that the
physical system does not show the instability suggested by the
mathematics. The mathematical structure thus has an infinitely greater complexity than the physical structure with
which it deals. In our elementary and classical theories we
have become used to discarding perhaps one-half of the
results of the mathematics, as when we discard the negative
or imaginary roots of equations as having no physical  significance, but here we retain only an infinitesimal part of the
mathematical results, and except for a few isolated singular
points relegate the entire mathematical structure to a ghostly
domain with no physical relevance. A vivid appreciation of
this situation will make it rather difficult, I believe, to maintain a conviction of the organic similarity of mathematics

and physical experience, or of the esoterically fundamental position of mathematics. With such an appreciation, Jeans would never have uttered his classical anthropomorphism "God is a mathematician."

The way in which conclusions about the properties of the mathematical model are to be translated into conclusions about the corresponding physical system is not capable of specification with logical precision, as we have already seen must always be the case when we apply probability theory to any concrete physical situation. We are really concerned more with an art than a science, an art which is to be learned only by observation of the way the inventers of the theory do it. The art is not a difficult one to learn, and the lack of logical precision is not disturbing in practice, because the expectation that observable results will ever arise from this lack of precision is of the same small order of magnitude as our expectation that we may some day see a pail of water freeze on the fire. What we have here is a special sort of intellectual tool, of great utility in meeting the situations of practice. The fact that the mode of action of this tool cannot be reduced to completely logical terms we have seen to be a commentary, not only on the character of the tool, but also on our preconception that all mental methods of satisfactorily meeting actual situations must be reducible to logically rigorous operations.

The intuitive applicability of the wave mechanics point of view, even admitting that the lack of rigor is not damaging in practice, must be limited, as we have stated, to systems which can be thought of approximately as one of an ensemble. This means a small system, such that many other systems similar to it could be set up, and such that experiments on the system could be indefinitely repeated. This is the case par excellence with the molecules and the simple apparatus of our physical laboratories, the action of which has been successfully treated in terms of the theory. The theory is intrinsically incapable of application to the entire universe; this again it seems to me constitutes a merit. For imagine what would be involved in a theory which was comprehensive enough to embrace in a single coordinating point of view the entire universe. Such a theory would have to exist in the mind of the theorizer; but his mind is also a part of the universe, so that the theory would have to involve a theory of the theory, and so on in never ending regression. A complete theory is thus intrinsically impossible. Or, putting the matter in another way, I believe that the "truth" of such a theory would have no operational meaning, as a little consideration will suggest. We would appear again to encounter a fundamental intellectual limitation; the only sort of theory possible is a partial theory of limited aspects of the whole. It thus seems that there is a fundamental incompatibility of point of view between one of the avowed aims of general relativity theory and wave mechanics.

In addition to the merit of providing a qualitative parallel to error, wave mechanics has the great merit that it exhibits a very close formal connection between the theory and the things that we do, that is, it is formally a thoroughgoing operational theory. This end is achieved by labelling some of the mathematical symbols "operators," "observables," etc. But in spite of the existence of a mathematical symbolism of this sort, the exact corresponding physical manipulations are often obscure, at least in the sense that it is not obvious how one would construct an idealized laboratory apparatus for making any desired sort of measurement. I think there is significance in the difficulty which my theoretical friends find in suggesting what sort of apparatus they would set up in the laboratory in order to answer such questions as: "Can $e$, or $m$, or $h$ be measured separately with unlimited precision by a single experiment, or may they be measured simultaneously in a single experiment?" Or what is the apparatus in terms of which any arbitrary "observable" of Dirac acquires its physical meaning? I think it will be granted by most theoretical physicists that there are situations of this sort which have not yet been thought completely through. Since we are now prepared to admit that the correspondence between mathematics and experience is never a one to one correspondence, so that because a mathematical theory accomplishes successfully one-half of what we would like to have it there is no certainty or even a high probability that it will accomplish the other half, I think we are justified in a certain amount of disquietude in the face of any situation that has not been thought through completely.

The mere fact that such a debate is possible as that carried out on the one hand by Einstein, Podolsky and Rosen,[2] and on the other hand by Bohr,[3] increases our disquietude. Einstein, Podolsky and Rosen, in their article on physical reality and wave mechanics, take the position that because wave mechanics does not act according to their idea of the way that it should act from general philosophical considerations it must therefore be incomplete. Bohr, on the other hand, takes the position that our preconceived views as to the nature of physical reality must be modified in view of the recently discovered fact that a mathematical theory is possible which agrees with physical experience in all pertinent particulars but which takes a modified attitude as to the nature of "reality." It seems to me that Bohr's argument is essentially an argument from simplicity. No mathematical theory is unique, so that it cannot be certain that there might not be other ways of reaching agreement with experience that might perhaps retain the old concept of reality. All we can say at present is that no simple method of doing this is in sight.

[2] A. Einstein, B. Podolsky and N. Rosen, *Phys. Rev.*, 47, 777, 1935.
[3] N. Bohr, *Phys. Rev.*, 48, 696, 1935.

The weakness of the position of Einstein, Podolsky and Rosen is that they assume that our inherited ideas cannot be replaced by better ones. All of which is consistent with the recognition that what we mean by physical reality is to a large extent a matter of convention and convenience.

The number of papers in the recent literature which have been inspired by the discussion between Einstein and Bohr is itself an illuminating commentary on the way in which theories get written. It is obvious enough that the epistemological consequences now appearing were not deliberately put into the theory by its founders. What we are doing is to discover in a mathematical machinery originally specifically set up to correlate physical phenomena in a certain range of magnitude implications with regard to various epistemological matters. It is not easy to discover exactly what these implications are, as shown by the lack of agreement of various writers, but it is at any rate evident that modifications of earlier points of view are demanded. The fact that modifications of the earlier epistemology are demanded is no argument against the new, if it can be proved that the new is also consistent with experience *within the limit of experimental error*. Such a proof does as a matter of fact at the present time seem possible. The recognition that more than one epistemology is possible, which comes out of such an analysis, constitutes an important step forward. The only conclusion which it seems to me is justified here is that one is free to adopt the epistemology of wave mechanics if it is convenient; the theoretical physicist having much concern with the mathematical machinery will doubtless adopt this epistemology, because it is obviously convenient for him to weld as many of his working tools as possible into a coherent whole. But the mere fact that a mathematical theory built for one purpose has been found by experiment to involve a permissible epistemology must not, I believe, lead to the conviction that the new epistemology is necessarily more "correct" than the one which it replaces. One who believes in the existence somewhere "out there" of an ultimately correct theory will doubtless see significance in the fact that a mathematical theory making better connection with experiment also demands a revised and permissible epistemology, but in the minds of the more cynical of the non-elect the word "luck" may rise in this connection.

The epistemological implications in wave mechanics are, I believe, similar in a number of respects to those which would have been demanded by a serious acceptance of the universal applicability of the concepts of statistical mechanics, particularly the probability concepts. The epistemological implications in statistical mechanics have not, however, ever been elaborated.

Wave mechanics marks a great advance over former theories in its recognition that the act of observation is an essential feature in any physical situation. In the background of this recognition there appears to be a curious and perhaps unavoidable combination of physics and philosophy. The recognition that knowledge of a system, without which no theory is possible, is meaningless unless there is an observer, is philosophical in spirit. This philosophical recognition formerly appeared to be without physical pertinence and could be merely disregarded, but the new physical point of view of wave mechanics means that it can no longer be ignored, for if there is an observer there must of course be an act of observation, and the thesis of the new physical theory is that no act of observation can be performed without interfering with the system in a manner not capable of complete control. Up to the present, many theoretical physicists have occupied themselves with following out the consequences of the uncontrollable interference associated with the act of observation. This, it seems to me, can be only the beginning of the program and eventually we shall not be able to stop short of analyzing the observer as well as the act of observation. It may perhaps be hopeless ever to expect a mathematical formulation of the observer; the fact that the theory is itself a creature of the brain of the observer who is trying to formulate a theory which shall include his own brain would lead one to expect mathematical difficulties.

But it seems to me that there are certain questions which will have to be faced at least qualitatively. The reason for this is that up to the present any precise description of what we do in making the measurements by which the various concepts of wave mechanics acquire meaning has involved a reduction of everything to classical terms. For example, the apparatus is eventually to be made heavy so that we can get up to the scale of ordinary experience. Our meanings are thus ultimately to be sought in the realm of classical experience. This procedure, extended so as to include the observer as an essential part, must at present at least involve the thesis that the brain of the observer can be exhaustively described in purely classical terms. This I think would be committing ourselves much further than most of us would be willing to go. When one considers the infinite precision of thought demanded by logic and mathematics, and also the fact that this thought is associated with a finite aggregation of matter, I think one must hesitate to maintain that the necessary physical processes never reach down far enough into the small-scale structure of the brain to encounter quantum phenomena again.

If we are ever successful in including the observer as part of the system, I think it is obvious that errors (that is, blunders) by the observer must find their explanation on the classical level, for this sort of error can be given meaning only in terms of the indefinite repetition of an experiment, and indefinite repetitions are not unrestrictedly possible on the quantum level.

We have seen that the unanalyzable probability which wave mechanics introduces as elementary can be a property only of the mathematical model, because the concept of probability is logically never applicable to a concrete physical system. There is another important limitation on the physical applicability of the idea of "chance" or probability on the elementary level. In our first discussion of probability we reduced everything to the observation that empirically it had been found impossible to predict certain types of events, such as the tossing of a coin; such events were described as being "chance" events, or as a matter of words we could say that the fall of the coin was "governed" by chance. But notice that these unpredictable events must be embedded in a matrix of regularity and familiarity; otherwise we would not even have the means for defining or describing the event. "Chance" has no meaning except in a setting of order. It would be physically meaningless to say that *all* events on the elementary level are chance events, or that chance rules the universe at the elementary level. The most that we could have would be the applicability of chance to *some* of the events at this level. This, of course, is actually what happens; one of a conjugate pair must be exactly known if the other is subject to complete chance.

There are still other places in wave mechanics where there seems to be a dualism, at present unresolved, between the classical and the new points of view. Consider, for example, the fundamental equations in Schrödinger's form. The independent variables are space and time coordinates; what is the physical meaning of these, how shall we measure them, and what are they the coordinates of? Notice in the first place that points in space are not identifiable as such and have no physical meaning, but only points marked by the presence of material particles. We cannot do less than suppose the coordinate points are marked by the smallest possible material particle. The smallest material particle is perhaps the electron, and this has no fixed abode, but its location is a probability matter determined by the equations themselves. The variables of the equations, although called space and time variables, thus do not have their ostensible physical significance, but are purely constructional quantities used in the mathematical model. In particular there is no limitation whatever on the precision with which we may assume we know these mathematical coordinates; in this respect the space and time coordinates are like classical space and time.

The present tendency to seek all our meanings on the classical level, as by making the measuring apparatus heavy, involves, I believe, the necessity for a reexamination of purely classical points of view and a more searching analysis than appears to have been explicitly made. It must not be forgotten that by proper design we can bring quantum phenomena up to the classical level. By properly coupling a Geiger counter to a speck of radioactive matter it would be possible to blow up a battleship, and we could never give any account of the catastrophe in classical terms. As another example, consider the experiment conventionally used to illustrate the Heisenberg principle of indetermination, namely a simultaneous measurement of the position and momentum of a particle. The operations in terms of which position and momentum have their meaning are specified in classical terms. It seems to be characteristic of any adequate specification of an operation in classical terms that the time and place of performing the operation must be given, for otherwise we would not know exactly what to do. But if time and place must be exactly specified in fixing the operations of the measurements, then by the indetermination principle itself we no longer have a free choice of the accuracy with which we shall measure momentum and energy, whereas the possibility of a free choice as to whether momentum and energy shall be measured with accuracy is basic to the wave mechanics point of view. One solution of the dilemma would again be that the time and place which occur in the specification of classical operations are different sorts of thing from the time and place of the Heisenberg principle. Or another solution would be that from the classical point of view we are here concerned with a group of operations for measuring position, for example, from which the time element is abstracted, rather than with a single definite operation. But analysis, which I believe has never been attempted, would be required to show the possibility or consequences of modifying in this way the concept of position, for if the operations are modified the concept is modified. Position defined in terms of a definite operation performed at a specifiable time is not the same as position defined in terms of operations which may be freely made whenever the impulse moves one. Even if the time at which the operation is performed need not be specified, the temporal aspect cannot be entirely absent from the specification of the operation, for the operation is an activity, performed in time, and must consist of parts performed in a specified sequence in time. I think that other examples could be found of operations which have not yet been analyzed sufficiently to answer all questions that could be asked from even the classical point of view.

The potential energy function in the neighborhood of an elementary charge is still assumed to have the classical value and to vary inversely as the distance. It is true that this potential energy is recognizably a mathematical construction, because there is no direct operational method of finding whether this is actually the form of the potential function or not. Nevertheless it has always been a matter of surprise to me that it has been found necessary to carry the classical concept so far into what one would be inclined to call the heart of the wave mechanics domain.

A question closely connected with the potential energy of the nucleus is that of the meaning of the electric and magnetic field. On the classical, large-scale level, the operational meaning of the field is to be found in idealized experiments with elementary charges, which in the limit have to be made vanishingly small. This procedure of course cannot be extended to the quantum domain, and the physical significance of the field at this level is not at all obvious. It appears as if we were dealing here with a purely formal construction.

It is probable that wave mechanics, like any other theory that proceeds from assumptions that cannot be given complete physical meaning by any sort of operational control, will involve certain consequences beyond the reach of experimental check, as for example the classical kinetic theory of gases involved the consequence that it was not physically impossible for a pail of water to freeze on the fire. A consequence of this sort is involved in the treatment by wave mechanics of a photon as a material particle. In my analysis of the concept of light in the *Logic of Modern Physics* I emphasized the point of view that there was absolutely no physical evidence to compel us to accept the picture of light as a "thing travelling." This picture was merely a convenience in thinking, because it made simpler the calculation of certain consequences. But if light is "really" a thing travelling, then our ordinary way of thinking would lead us to expect interference effects between two crossed beams of light similar to the interference effects between two crossed beams of electrons. Now the mathematics of the wave mechanical description of a "stream" of photons does demand the existence of physical phenomena of this character. Numerical calculation shows, however, that even in the most intense radiational field in the interior of the stars, the consequences of such interaction would be immeasurably small (verbal communication from Dr. H. Bethe). The question, therefore, whether light "really" consists of photons travelling, or whether photons are "really" particles, is without present physical meaning.

On the other hand, the difficulties which one encounters in trying to treat such a simple physical system as two narrow slits, one or the other of which may be covered at random, from the point of view of the photon as an entity that travels (this problem has been discussed by Pauli in his *Handbuch* article) would indicate that there are some phenomena which it is distinctly unprofitable to attempt to visualize from the point of view of the photon as a thing that travels. The mathematics apparently does not demand that the photon be treated as a "thing travelling": we seem to be at the point where we must learn how to get rid of this adventitious aid in thinking.

It is often said that wave mechanics involves a dualistic attitude toward the fundamental entities, electrons, etc., in the sense that some phenomena demand that the electrons be described as particles, and others that they be thought of as waves. This it seems to me is not quite an accurate way of describing the situation. The meaning of the fundamental $\Psi$ function of wave mechanics is that it determines the probability that we shall find at the place and time assumed in the function one of the fundamental particles (electrons or photons). Only certain aspects of the question have been considered as to whether we are justified in thinking of this elemental thing as a particle and even these considerations are not free from the suggestion of fundamental difficulties. The operational meaning of "particle" is not adequately specified, and no discussion is given as to how we may infer from whatever experimental evidence we can get that we really have a particle as distinguished from a system of waves. The particle seems to be assumed as an unanalyzable in the theory. Furthermore, it is surprising that the experimental operations in terms of which this ultimate particle is defined all seem to be large-scale operations, with classical implications. Wave mechanics assumes a particle rather than a wave as the unanalyzable, I think, because of a fundamental intellectual limitation. We seem to demand as the ultimate elements of thought discrete, identifiable things with no recognizable structure. I very much question whether one can even think of physical waves without assuming in his thought that the medium which carries the waves is itself composed of particles—for otherwise he has nothing to put his finger on by which he can tell whether he is now talking about the same medium that he did a moment ago or not. We have here another manifestation of the same intellectual characteristic that forces us to think in terms of words and intuitively recognizable concepts with fixed meanings.

I think wave mechanics would be embarrassed if it were pushed to specify too sharply what it meant by "particle." Although the electron is implicitly treated as a particle in the classical sense, it turns out that it must lack one very essential characteristic of the classical particle, namely individuality and identifiability. What can one mean by a particle without individuality? Wave mechanics deals with the situation by accepting the implications of the classical particle, and then superposing on this picture a special statistics, such that no new combination is counted when two particles exchange places, thus cancelling the effect of individuality. Not only is such a particle assumed as an unanalyzable, but no description seems to be attempted of the nature of the physical experience by which we recognize the presence of an unanalyzable of this character. It should be almost axiomatic that unanalyzables must be of such a character that they can be recognized intuitively; the unanalyzable of wave mechanics is a strange thing, and I find that I have no intuitive feeling for it.

In general, then, it seems to me that wave mechanics is less successful in bringing everything under a common point of view than one might expect from the way some of its expounders talk about it, and that we have in fact an apparently unresolvable mixture of classical and wave mechanical elements. There can eventually be no vital objection to such a mixture, provided the wave mechanical concepts can be made precise without involving a reduction to classical concepts, for as we have already seen, the only essential requirement is that the theory should be workable, and almost any mixture can be made workable with the help of enough special instructions contained in the "text." But too many special instructions in the text give the appearance of clumsiness, and when in addition the text is suppressed, as it almost always is, and wave mechanics is no exception, the difficulty of the theory is unnecessarily increased. I think that the esthetic motive, if nothing else, will prove sufficiently strong to ensure the continuation of effort to get a somewhat more homogeneous appearing theory.

The spectacle that wave mechanics presents from a detached and not technically mathematical viewpoint contains some surprising features. Consider the nature of the structure as we now have it in the light of the conceptual problem that originally presented itself. Our previous concepts had demonstrably failed to fit the new experimental situations, so that we were forced to devise new concepts. What have we done in the emergency? We still keep as our unanalyzable the particle of ordinary experience, but evade the issue of describing what we mean by a particle in a domain where ordinary concepts fail. It is true we get rid of some of the implications of our ordinary concept of identifiability by demanding that the particle shall obey a special statistics; but this appears to me to be something of a makeshift. The background against which the unanalyzables show up is a background not describable in terms of the ordinary concepts of space, time, and causality. We meet the situation by saying in effect that the old concepts shall still be one-half applicable to what happens on the elemental level and that the other shall be pure chance, that is, pure chaos. If the concept of localization applies exactly, the concept of momentum does not apply at all. In other words, since pure chance can have no meaning except with a background of order, we give the devil the maximum by letting him have one-half chance while we keep one-half order or one-half the old concepts. We account for the evolution of the ordinary concepts of space, time, and causality on the level of ordinary experience by postulating that the effect of the chaotic element gradually gets cancelled out as we proceed toward large-scale phenomena in virtue of the regularities of large numbers. Is this honestly, from a perfectly detached point of view, a very impressive performance? Is it not exactly the sort of compromise that we would have predicted in advance would be the only possible one if it should prove that we were incapable of inventing any vitally new way of thinking about small-scale things? Do we really think that a dualism of this kind says nearly as much about the structure of external nature as it does about the structure of our minds?

It is evident that we are not entirely satisfied with what we have got and that we are groping for some new way of thinking about small-scale things from the manner in which some people are handling the qualitative results of the mathematical analysis. It is certain that not all the qualitative points of view which have come out of the mathematics were deliberately put into the mathematics by the founders of the theory. I know by first-hand experience that in the experimental field the apparatus which one is designing may have properties that one did not envisage in the original design, and that one may stumble on important new things. Furthermore, the new thing that one stumbles on may then be reached more efficiently by some other design quite remote from the one that gave the idea. It would be surprising if very much the same sort of thing did not happen with mathematical theories. At any rate, with regard to wave mechanics, it seems to me to be an entirely defensible position to maintain that although some of the new points of view that have been qualitatively suggested by the mathematics were more or less incidental to the mathematics, they actually go much deeper, so that it is possible to glimpse through our present mathematics something much more fundamental beyond it, which we may ultimately be able to reach more directly. We have certainly come to a better understanding of the nature of causality and determinism under the spur of trying to interpret a mathematical theory which was developed from other points of view. The fact that we now recognize causality as a purely experimental question involves a deeper insight than went into the special mathematical analysis which gave rise to the recognition. To a number of persons the Heisenberg principle of indetermination has seemed evidence of something with deeper significance than a purely mathematical non-commutability of $p$ and $q$ numbers. One would like to find out how to handle this new principle intuitively, in its own right, divorced from the severe mathematical considerations that gave rise to it. Attempts to do this sort of thing have not been uncommon; perhaps the most elaborate is that of Lindemann.[4] I think

[4] F. A. Lindemann, *The Physical Significance of the Quantum Theory*, Oxford, Clarendon Press, 1932.

such attempts should be judged sympathetically, as experiments in thinking which may be enormously fruitful, instead
of harshly from the narrow point of view of the special
mathematical theory which happened to give the first
suggestion.

# X. IN CONCLUSION

FINALLY, we cast a brief glance in retrospect over the actual field of physical theory. Physical theory is incontestably an activity of human individuals. We might understand by physical theory the sum total of the theoretical activities of all individuals, but more profitably we have restricted ourselves to the usual meaning, namely the aggregate of the theorizing of *competent* individuals.

If anyone examines his own theoretical activity he will discover that there are two essentially different parts. There is a creative part: the discovery of new ideas, their critical examination and analysis, and acceptance or rejection. This activity demands the highest degree of self-conscious awareness on the part of the theorizer, and the product of this activity is in a peculiar sense a living thing. But fresh creation cannot occur very often, and the second and usually the major part of the theoretical activity of any individual consists in assimilating to himself the creative ideas of others. If the theory is to be vitally apprehended, so that it can be applied to fresh situations and be more than mere symbols written in a book, something is demanded akin to an act of fresh creation, but usually on a much lower plane. One's interest in the ideas of another may be restricted to acquiring sufficient mastery of them so that one can apply them in concrete situations in the same way that the inventor of the theory would have done.

In order to do this nothing more is required in many cases than that imitative facility which is placed at such a premium by our entire system of education. It is rare that one goes through the same process of critical appraisal in acquiring a theory that the inventor did in the first place. The reason for this may be difference of interest, already suggested, and in addition partly inferior ability, but more importantly, it may be sheer lack of time. The chewing of the cud and digestion demanded by satisfactory critical analysis is a slow process. There are certain questions into which no one individual can go with any depth of critical analysis and find time for other things. Certain results he has to accept vicariously in the conviction that if he took the time to make a careful analysis he would come to the same conclusions that he believes other people have come to whose integrity he respects. But no conviction acquired vicariously can be held with the security of a conviction acquired by personal rumination, as doubtless anyone can verify from his own experience. Physical theory in its highest, dynamic, vital development exists in the minds of only a handful of people. In the mind of the average individual we have in the first place a body of more or less vividly apprehended methods of procedure for dealing with a certain class of physical situations, which are accepted with confidence because by first-hand experience they have been found to yield correct results, and in the second place we have the arguments by which these methods of procedure are made understandable.

These arguments may be of all possible degrees of vividness; some of them have been analyzed with care and are held with confidence, others have not been thought through carefully but are held in the comfortable belief that they are all right and that some one must have examined them at some time. This comfortable conviction is usually highly inarticulate; just what the fundamental assumptions are that have been found satisfactory could not be stated, or who it was that made the examination, except in a general way one of the founders of the theory. It is easy to say to a fundamental question in wave mechanics: "I do not know the answer to that, but I suppose that Dirac or Bohr or Heisenberg has thought it through and knows the answer." The argument justifying this vicarious acceptance is that if there were any-thing wrong in the fundamentals it would have made trouble with some of the applications.

There is obviously great danger here, as there is in any situation which is not completely articulate and self-con-scious. There is particular danger if the inventor of the theory himself conceived the fundamental idea in a flash of inspira-tion, as often happens. Adequate critical examination in such cases must be difficult to attain. In any event it is rare for the founder of a theory to attempt to communicate all the steps which led him to the final theory, and physically impos-sible for him to analyze all the assumptions which went into it. It is natural that those assumptions which he analyzes with the greatest care are those which are specific to the particular theory, and the assumptions which he accepts with least self-conscious examination are those common to all human thought. Assumptions of this sort may not even be clearly recognized as such; these are the assumptions that everyone makes because of the temper of the times or because of a common heritage.

This volume has endeavored to direct attention to some of the more pervasive of these assumptions. Some of these carry indelibly the traces of their human origin. There are other evidences of the human origin of physical theory than merely the limitations imposed by lack of time, or by insufficient intellectual power, or by those cruder human traits such as a too self-seeking competitiveness. Man has never been a par-ticularly modest or self-deprecatory animal, and physical theory bears witness to this no less than many other important human activities. The idea that thought is the measure of all things, that there is such a thing as utter logical rigor, that conclusions can be drawn endowed with an inescapable neces-sity, that mathematics has an absolute validity and controls experience—these are not the ideas of a modest animal. Not only do our theories betray these somewhat bumptious traits of self-appreciation, but especially obvious through them all is the thread of incorrigible optimism so characteristic of human beings.

Every new theory as it arises believes in the flush of youth that it has the long sought goal; it sees no limits to its applicability, and believes that at last it is the fortunate theory to achieve the "right" answer. This was true of electron theory —perhaps some readers will remember a book called *The Electrical Theory of the Universe* by de Tunzelmann. It is true of general relativity theory with its belief that we can formulate a mathematical scheme that will extrapolate to all past and future time and the unfathomed depths of space. It has been true of wave mechanics, with its first enthusiastic claim a brief ten years ago that no problem had successfully resisted its attack provided the attack was properly made, and now the disillusion of age when confronted by the problems of the proton and the neutron. When will we learn that logic, mathematics, physical theory, are all only our inventions for formulating in compact and manageable form what we already know, and like all inventions do not achieve complete success in accomplishing what they were designed to do, much less complete success in fields beyond the scope of the original design, and that our only justification for hoping to penetrate at all into the unknown with these inventions is our past experience that sometimes we have been fortunate enough to be able to push on a short distance by acquired momentum?

# INDEX